Contents

Identifying more able mathematicians

What characteristics might gifted mathematicians display?

More able mathematicians are likely to have good powers of logic, reasoning and deduction, and will be able to hypothesise, experiment and categorise. This list of questions may be useful in establishing mathematical ability:

- Do they enjoy number puzzles?
- Do they show a good awareness of patterns and sequences?
- Do they ask interesting mathematical questions?
- Do they give explanations you may not have thought of?
- Are they good at solving problems?
- Are they good at applying knowledge in unfamiliar contexts?
- Do they like to choose their own methods?

This list is by no means exhaustive; there are many more characteristics that may be observed in gifted mathematicians, and many gifted children will display only some of these qualities. For example, a child who you believe to be a high achiever may not show advanced problem-solving skills. This may be because they don't yet know how to set about solving a problem, because they haven't learned the strategies required. You may find children who are gifted in just one or two areas of maths. For example, they may excel at calculation and number, but may not do so well at shape and space.

What about children who don't show any of these traits?

There may be gifted mathematicians in your class who do not display any of these characteristics. This could be due to one or more of these factors:

- lack of confidence
- unwillingness to stand out from their peers
- the desire to avoid 'extra' work
- an insufficiently stimulating learning environment
- lack of challenging activities
- lack of familiarity with basic number facts and skills
- language barriers
- problems with reading and/or writing.

What can be done to identify gifted mathematicians?

Here are a few suggestions of practical steps that can be taken:

- Ask parents and carers to supply information about any mathematical abilities they have noticed at home.
- Conduct a brief interview with children at the beginning of the school year to find out about their interests and anything they think they are especially good at.
- Keep a portfolio of particularly good work completed either at home or in school. This will help to assess progress and spot patterns.
- Testing can provide evidence of high ability, but you should be aware that some more able or gifted children may not perform well in tests, and many factors can affect children's performance in a test environment.

The identification–provision cycle

A two-way process of identification and provision is needed. You will not be able to observe exceptional abilities in children unless they are given the opportunity to demonstrate them. Activities must be provided that challenge children and allow them the scope to show what they can do. In this way, appropriate provision leads to identification, which in turn allows you to make better provision.

How can a stimulating learning environment be created?

It is important that more able children are asked probing and open-ended questions. These will allow you to assess and extend their understanding, get them to think more deeply, and lead them to continue their explorations. Here are some examples of the types of question you might ask:

- What do you think will happen if …?
- How many different ways can you …?
- Is it always true that …?
- Why?
- What patterns can you see?
- Why did you choose to work it out like that?
- Why do you think this happens?
- How do you know that?
- Can you make up a rule?

It is also important to create an atmosphere in which children feel they are able to ask questions, and have access to resources to find the answers. One practical thing you can do is to create a 'Challenge corner': an area of the classroom where you can set out maths resources, puzzles, prompts and questions for children to explore. This should be accessible by all children in the class, giving everyone the opportunity to challenge themselves.

What are 'challenge' activities?

'Challenging' work can be defined as something difficult that requires the learner to learn something new. For children to enjoy a challenging activity there must be something about it that motivates them. For example, it could be about a subject that they are particularly interested in, or it could be placed in a meaningful context, with a goal that has nothing to do with completing a page of calculations. The level of challenge must be just right – it must stretch them without being so difficult that children are demotivated and want to give up. The best challenge activities will allow different levels of outcome, so that a wide range of children can succeed at them.

More able or gifted children need to be given opportunities to:

- exercise their curiosity and explore new ideas
- choose their own ways of working and representing their results
- ask questions and find the answers
- make conjectures and test them out
- discuss their ideas with adults and other children
- reflect on their own work.

What thinking skills should more able children be using?

More able children need to be given opportunities to access their higher-order thinking skills. Bloom's Taxonomy identifies six levels of thinking:

- knowledge – the acquisition and recall of facts
- comprehension – the ability to describe what you know in your own words
- application – the application of what you have learned in context
- analysis – for example, categorising things and identifying patterns
- synthesis – the creation of new ideas or products
- evaluation – the evaluation of ideas, processes and products.

The first three are generally thought of as lower-order skills, although application requires a deeper level of thinking than the first two. If you can plan activities that incorporate the three higher-order thinking skills, children will be challenged.

What is *Abacus Evolve Challenge*?

Abacus Evolve Challenge is designed to stretch and motivate more able mathematicians. The activities are creative and engaging, and offer opportunities for written, verbal and practical work. Using and applying skills are practised throughout, with plenty of open-ended investigations and problem solving. Speaking and listening skills are promoted through the high proportion of paired and group work.

Which children is *Challenge* for?

Challenge is not just for those children who would be classed as 'gifted'. The activities have been written with the whole of the 'top table' in mind. Differentiation by outcome is often possible because of the open-ended nature of the activities, and the teacher notes accompanying the activities usually suggest ways to differentiate further.

What types of enrichment and extension are provided?

Breadth – allows children to experience additional material outside of the core offering, rehearse ideas in different contexts, and make connections between areas of maths.

Depth – is achieved by asking children to delve deeper into the concepts. It is about thinking intellectually.

Pace – refers to speed in covering the curriculum and can result in achievement at a level exceptional for the age range.

What types of activity are provided?

Adult-led – these activities allow children to work with an adult. There are two adult-led activities per two-week block.

Practise – these activities allow children to practise what they have learned with the rest of the class, at a higher level.

Discover – these activities allow children to learn about things like famous mathematicians and ancient number systems.

Investigate – these activities allow children to explore a concept freely, asking questions, looking for patterns and drawing conclusions.

When should the *Challenge* activities be used?

There are 90 activities per Year; six for every two-week block. They are intended to be used by small groups of children in the part of the maths lesson when the class is split into groups for differentiated work. This allows the more able children to be included in the whole-class parts of the lesson.

What level of adult support is needed?

The *Challenge* resources have been designed with effective classroom management in mind. Four of the activities in each two-week block can be carried out by children without adult support, allowing you to focus on the other groups. Some of these will require a couple of minutes to get the group started on the activity, but after this children should be able to continue unaided.

Two of the activities in each two-week block require adult support, so that your able and gifted children have the benefits of adult input.

How does *Challenge* fit alongside the *Abacus Evolve* maths scheme?

The *Challenge* activities are organised using the same blocked structure as *Abacus Evolve*. You can use the *Abacus Evolve* weekly plans, and fit the *Challenge* activities into these. *Abacus Evolve* objectives are referenced for each activity, and these will help you to decide which core activities to run them alongside. If you also have the *Challenge* Module of I-Planner Online, you will be able to see the *Challenge* activities allocated to suitable days in the weekly plans.

It is intended that the more able children join in with the whole-class parts of the lesson: the mental oral starter, the main teaching activity, and the plenary. When the rest of the class is split up into 1-dot, 2-dot and 3-dot groups to do Textbook activities or practical activities, you can give your top group a *Challenge* activity that fits in well with what the rest of the class are doing.

Can I use *Challenge* with another maths scheme or my own planning?

Although the *Challenge* activities complement *Abacus Evolve* activities, they are not specifically linked to them, so there is no dependence on any part of the *Abacus Evolve* scheme. The *Challenge* activities can be used to accompany any other maths scheme or your own planning. You can search for *Challenge* activities that fit your teaching by looking at the Renewed Framework objectives in the Teacher Guide. All of the Renewed Framework objectives are covered by the *Challenge* activities.

Using the *Challenge* resources

What resources are in the *Challenge* range?
Each Year includes:
- a Teacher Guide
- a Textbook
- an I-Planner Online Module.

Teacher Guide
The Teacher Guide contains detailed notes to accompany each activity. The information provided includes:
- Suggested group size and adult support
- Resources required (Textbook pages, Photocopy Masters and other resources)
- *Abacus Evolve* objectives
- Renewed Framework objectives
- A description of the activity
- 'Extra help': ideas for differentiating at a lower level
- 'Further extension': ideas for differentiating at a higher level
- 'If you have time': ideas for continuing the activity
- Background maths information for the non-specialist teacher
- 'Be aware': things to watch out for, such as common misconceptions
- Outcomes for the activity, given in child-friendly language
- Ideas for other resources to support the activity, such as useful websites.

Textbook
There are five Textbook pages per two-week block, so nearly every activity has an accompanying Textbook page. The pages are colourful and engaging, and they include the following features:
- speech bubbles to indicate opportunities for discussion
- an Extra activity at the bottom of each page for children who finish early.

The Textbook pages are not just intended for children to use individually. They are often suitable for paired or group work.

I-Planner Online
The *Abacus Evolve* I-Planner is a powerful online tool that provides ready-to-use weekly, medium-term and yearly plans that are completely flexible. It can save hours of planning time, but allows you to adapt the plans to meet the exact needs of your class. The *Challenge* module of I-Planner for each Year includes an extra column in the weekly plans in which you can see all the *Challenge* activities allocated to suitable days. This allows you to plan the *Challenge* activities seamlessly into your maths lessons.

What support is provided for assessing the children?
The adult-led activities are ideal for day-to-day observational assessment, as they provide plenty of opportunities to work closely with the children and ask probing questions to ascertain their level of understanding.

The charts on pages 8–11 of this book show the Assessment Foci from the Assessing Pupils' Progress guidelines, and the *Challenge* activities that can be used to provide evidence towards this type of assessment.

On pages 106–115 of this book you will find three end-of-term investigative activities. These will allow you to assess how well children use and apply the skills they have built up over the term.

Icon guide

Group size

 Children working individually, without an adult

 Children working in pairs, without an adult

 Children working in groups, without an adult

 Children working in groups, with an adult

Type of resource

 Textbook

Photocopy Master

Additional resources

Type of enrichment/extension

 Breadth

Depth

Pace

Type of activity

 Adult-led

Practise

 Discover

 Investigate

Support for Assessing Pupil's Progress

If you are using Assessing Pupil's Progress to assess children, you may find this chart helpful when deciding which of the *Challenge* activities could be used to provide evidence towards each Assessment Focus.

We do not recommend that you use every activity to make an assessment. It is also important to recognise that a full assessment cannot be made on the basis of the *Challenge* activities alone; you will need to draw on other sources of information as well. We would advise that in each block of work you use this chart as guidance towards choosing one activity to assess against APP criteria, to complement other day-to-day or periodic assessments.

Most of the Year 3 *Challenge* activities should give children the opportunity to work at a secure or high Level 3, and in some cases at a low Level 4.

	Ma1 Using and applying mathematics		
	Problem solving	Communicating	Reasoning
Level 4			• A3.5 Think of a number
Level 3	• A1.4 Sheets of stamps • B1.3 Magic squares • B1.4 Tetrominoes • E1.6 Doubling and halving shapes • A2.3 Timelines • B2.5 The Soma cube • B2.6 Prisms and anti-prisms • C2.1 Calibrating capacities • C2.2 Calculating capacities • E2.5 Escape from 100 • A3.6 Four square • C3.4 Time facts • C3.5 Calendars • D3.3 Cryptarithm puzzles • E3.1 Multiplication arithmagons • E3.4 Repeated halving	• A1.1 Growing on trees • B1.5 Tile patterns • B1.6 M C Escher • C1.2 Body measures • A2.4 Counting sequences • D2.2 Squares to zero • D2.5 Magic numbers • A3.4 Fibonacci's pattern • B3.5 Routes around shapes • B3.6 Mathematical worms • C3.6 Logic tracks	• A1.2 Making moves • A1.3 Make a number • D1.1 Disc numbers • E1.5 Function machines • A2.1 Rounding • A2.4 Counting sequences • B2.4 Making 3D stars • D2.2 Squares to zero • D2.5 Magic numbers • D2.6 Digital roots • E2.4 Multiples of 3, 6 and 9 • A3.3 Take three numbers • C3.6 Logic tracks • D3.1 Three by three squares • D3.2 Pentacircles and hexacircles • E3.5 Matching fractions, matching money

Ma2 Number

		Numbers and the number system	Fractions, decimals, percentages and ratio	Operations, relationships between them
Level 4		• E2.2 Ants and elephants • C3.3 Ant and elephant weights • E3.3 Multiplying and dividing by 10, 100 and 1000		• E3.2 Multiplication tables 2
Level 3		• A1.1 Growing on trees • A1.6 Egyptian numbers • A2.1 Rounding • A2.2 Ordering numbers • D2.4 Hundreds and thousands linking cards • A3.1 Rounding up and down	• C1.3 Making journeys • E1.4 Fraction sentences • E2.6 Fractions of quantities • E3.4 Repeated halving • E3.5 Matching fractions, matching money	• E1.1 Linking multiplication and division • E1.2 Multiplication grids • E1.3 Multiplication investigation • E2.1 Multiplication linking cards • E2.3 Missing-number multiplications and divisions • B3.2 Multiplication and division cross-number puzzles • E3.1 Multiplication arithmagons

Ma2 Number

	Mental methods	Solving numerical problems	Written and calculator methods
Level 4	• B2.3 Complements linking cards • E3.2 Multiplication grids 2	• A3.2 Rounding and estimating • A3.5 Think of a number • C3.2 Map of Jersey • D3.6 Subtracting money amounts	• D3.6 Subtracting money amounts
Level 3	• A1.2 Making moves • A1.3 Make a number • A1.4 Sheets of stamps • B1.1 Circular counting stick • D1.2 Boxed number games • E1.1 Linking multiplication and division • E1.2 Multiplication grids • E1.3 Multiplication investigation • A2.5 Counting on and back • B2.1 Using multiples to add and subtract • D2.1 Higher number squares • D2.3 Addition walls • D2.6 Digital roots • E2.1 Multiplication linking cards • B3.1 Doubling, doubling and doubling • B3.2 Multiplication and division cross-number puzzles • D3.5 Changing subtractions	• A1.5 Calculator rules • B1.2 Rows of houses • D1.1 Disc numbers • E1.5 Function machines • A2.6 Olympic rings • B2.2 Adding and subtracting • C2.3 Record times • E2.6 Fractions of quantities	• D1.3 Subtraction cross-number puzzles • A3.3 Take three numbers • D3.1 Three by three squares • D3.2 Pentacircles and hexacircles • D3.3 Cryptarithm puzzles • D3.4 Finding differences • D3.5 Changing subtractions

Ma3 Shape, space and measures

	Properties of shape	Properties of position and movement	Measures
Level 4	• B2.5 The Soma cube • B2.6 Prisms and anti-prisms		• D1.6 Matching times
Level 3	• B1.4 Tetrominoes • B2.4 Making 3D stars	• B1.5 Tile patterns • B1.6 M C Escher • B3.5 Routes around shapes • B3.6 Mathematical worms	• C1.1 Estimating measurements • C1.2 Body measures • D1.5 How much time? • C2.1 Calibrating capacities • C2.2 Calculating capacities • C2.3 Record times • A3.6 Four square • B3.4 Hands on a clock

Ma4 Handling data

	Processing and representing data	Interpreting data
Level 4	• C2.4 Frequency tables	• C2.4 Frequency tables • C2.5 Box-and-whisker plots
Level 3	• C1.4 Designing a survey • C1.6 Minibeasts • C2.6 Star names and real names	• C1.4 Designing a survey • C1.5 Stem-and-leaf diagrams

Talk Maths Extra pupil software

Abacus Evolve *Talk Maths Extra* will reinforce key maths skills and get children talking about maths.

1 Place value 	Make target numbers by adding multiples of 10 or 100 to 2-digit or 3-digit numbers.	**2 Counting in 10s and 100s** 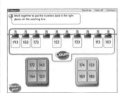
Complete a sequence counting on or back in 10s or 100s from a 3-digit number.	**3 Number triangle** 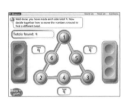	Place numbers so that each side has the same total.
4 Symmetry 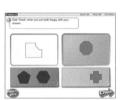	Work out what shape has been cut out of the centre of a piece of paper folded twice.	**5 Ordering clocks** 
Place non-consecutive o'clock, half past and quarter past times in order.	**6 Addition facts** 	Add multiples of 5 to make multiples of 100.
7 Shape detective 	Find a mystery shape by eliminating shapes based on clues.	**8 Place value** 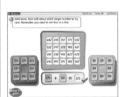
Make target numbers by adding multiples of 10 to 2-digit or 3-digit numbers.	**9 Addition and subtraction** 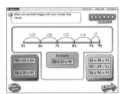	Find the number sentence that matches an addition or subtraction shown on a number line.
10 Counting in 3s 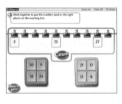	Fill in missing numbers in a sequence of numbers starting from 3 or 30 and counting on or back in 3s.	**11 Rounding** 
Place non-consecutive numbers on a rack, aiming to end up with the numbers in order.	**12 Number detective** 	Find a mystery number by eliminating numbers based on clues.
13 Difference 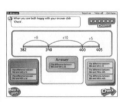	Find the sentence that matches a difference shown on a number line.	**14 Word problems** 
Fill in numbers in a word problem to make a correct multiplication or division.	**15 Ordering fractions** 	Place whole numbers, fractions and mixed numbers in order.
16 Buried treasure 	Follow clues to position items on a map, then find the buried treasure.	**17 Units of measurement** 
Select smaller units of length, capacity and weight to make up a larger unit.	**18 Carroll diagram** 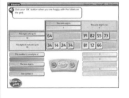	Place numbers onto a Carroll diagram, then choose labels to fit the numbers in the boxes.

This chart shows which *Talk Maths Extra* activities could be used to extend some of the *Challenge* activities. The 4-dot version of each *Talk Maths Extra* activity is likely to be the most suitable for your children.

Challenge activity	Related *Talk Maths Extra* activities
A1.1 Growing on trees	1 Place value
A1.2 Making moves	2 Counting in 10s and 100s
A1.3 Make a number	6 Addition facts
A1.4 Sheets of stamps	12 Number detective, 14 Word problems
B1.1 Circular counting stick	14 Word problems
B1.2 Rows of houses	3 Number triangle
B1.3 Magic squares	3 Number triangle
B1.4 Tetrominoes	7 Shape detective
B1.5 Tile patterns	4 Symmetry
D1.3 Subtraction cross-number puzzles	13 Difference
D1.4 Clocks through time	5 Ordering clocks
D1.6 Matching times	5 Ordering clocks
E1.1 Linking multiplication and division	14 Word problems
E1.2 Multiplication grids	14 Word problems
E1.3 Multiplication investigation	14 Word problems
E1.4 Fraction sentences	15 Ordering fractions
A2.1 Rounding	11 Rounding
A2.2 Ordering numbers	11 Rounding
A2.3 Timelines	2 Counting in 10s and 100s, 11 Rounding
A2.4 Counting sequences	2 Counting in 10s and 100s
A2.5 Counting on and back	2 Counting in 10s and 100s
B2.1 Using multiples to add and subtract	1 Place value, 6 Addition facts, 8 Place value
B2.2 Adding and subtracting	6 Addition facts, 8 Place value
B2.3 Complements linking cards	6 Addition facts
C2.2 Calculating capacities	17 Units of measurement
D2.1 Higher number squares	9 Addition and subtraction
D2.4 Hundreds and thousands linking cards	1 Place value
D2.5 Magic numbers	3 Number triangle, 9 Addition and subtraction
E2.1 Multiplication linking cards	14 Word problems
E2.4 Multiples of 3, 6 and 9	10 Counting in 3s
E2.5 Escape from 100	12 Number detective
A3.1 Rounding up and down	11 Rounding
A3.2 Rounding and estimating	8 Place value, 11 Rounding
A3.3 Take three numbers	13 Difference
B3.1 Doubling, doubling and doubling	12 Number detective
B3.5 Routes around shapes	16 Buried treasure
B3.6 Mathematical worms	16 Buried treasure
C3.1 British cities	16 Buried treasure
C3.6 Logic tracks	12 Number detective, 18 Carroll diagram
D3.4 Finding differences	13 Difference
D3.5 Changing subtractions	13 Difference
D3.6 Subtracting money amounts	9 Addition and subtraction, 13 Difference
E3.1 Multiplication arithmagons	14 Word problems
E3.2 Multiplication grids 2	14 Word problems
E3.5 Matching fractions, matching money	15 Ordering fractions

Abacus Evolve *Solve the Problem* will challenge children with rich, open-ended problems that draw on a range of mathematical strategies.

Find the Tiger

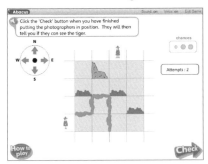

A tiger is hiding somewhere in the jungle. Children move two photographers, each with different vantage points, around the jungle grid. They use feedback from the photographers and try to locate the tiger in as few attempts as possible.

Around the World

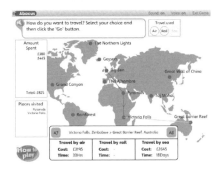

Children plan their own around-the-world trip. They start and finish in the UK, and can visit up to seven attractions. Their budget should not exceed £10 000 and their trip should include air, rail and sea travel.

Sorting Presents

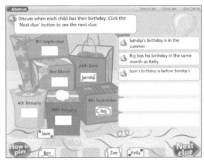

Six birthday presents are shown, each labelled with a birthday date but no name. Children have to follow the clues in order to identify which name label belongs to which present. Children can play the game twice; the second time they will receive a different set of clues.

Alien Athletics

Children take the role of team manager in the alien athletics. They select an alien athlete to enter an event, using the athletes' personal best data to help them. The aim is to beat the computer's athletes and win each competition.

School Trip

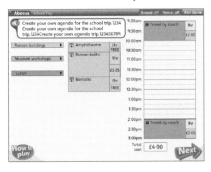

Children plan a day trip connected with a topic on the Romans. They select activities and organise them into a timetable that fits the time and budget available. They need to decide how best to spend their time and money.

Trolley Dash

Children have a set amount of time to spend in a supermarket, filling the trolley with goods. They need to plan their routes carefully in order to reach the checkout with the maximum value of goods in their trolley before the time runs out.

This chart shows which *Solve the Problem* activities could be used to extend some of the *Challenge* activities. The *Solve the Problem* activities are suitable for all ability levels, as children can set their own problems.

Challenge activity	Related *Solve the Problem* activities
A1.1 Growing on trees	Around the World
C1.2 Body measures	Alien Athletics
D1.5 How much time?	Alien Athletics, School Trip
D1.6 Matching times	School Trip
A2.1 Rounding	Around the World, Trolley Dash
B2.1 Using multiples to add and subtract	Around the World
B2.2 Adding and subtracting	Around the World
B2.3 Complements linking cards	School Trip
C2.2 Calculating capacities	Alien Athletics
C2.3 Record times	Sorting Presents, Alien Athletics
C2.5 Box-and-whisker plots	Alien Athletics
D2.4 Hundreds and thousands linking cards	Around the World
A3.2 Rounding and estimating	Around the World
B3.5 Routes around shapes	Find the Tiger
B3.6 Mathematical worms	Find the Tiger
C3.1 British cities	Find the Tiger
C3.3 Ant and elephant weights	Alien Athletics
C3.4 Time facts	Sorting Presents
C3.5 Calendars	Sorting Presents
D3.6 Subtracting money amounts	School Trip

Summary

Y3 ☆ A1.1

Growing on trees

Individuals, pairs or groups working independently

Year 3 Challenge Textbook page 3

Year 3 Challenge PCMs 1 and 2

Abacus Evolve objectives

- Read and write numbers up to 1000 in figures and words
- Count on in 5s to 100, and in 50s to 1000
- Add and subtract a multiple of 10 to and from a 3-digit number, crossing 100
- Add and subtract a multiple of 100 to and from a 4-digit number, crossing 1000
- Extend understanding that subtraction is the inverse of addition

Framework objectives

- Read, write and order whole numbers to at least 1000 and position them on a number line; count on from and back to zero in single-digit steps or multiples of 10
- Add or subtract mentally combinations of one-digit and two-digit numbers
- Identify patterns and relationships involving numbers or shapes, and use these to solve problems

Teacher notes

Preparation
Photocopy PCMs 1 and 2, one copy of each per child.

Getting started
Check that children understand how the code-hexagon below the tree informs them what number to write in each space.

Activity
Children work from Textbook page 3 and record their answers on PCMs 1 and 2. They use two rules to fill in the numbers in a tree-shaped arrangement of hexagons, and then go back and find the missing four rules. Children then compare their trees. They should notice how the patterns work in all six directions, and recognise that inverse rules apply for opposite directions. They should also notice that hexagons to the left or right of each other are affected by a combination of the rules.
Children then complete a second tree, before going on to make up their own rules for two more trees on PCM 2.

If you have time
Children will find it useful to discuss their patterns. Often children will have different insights that combine to give all of them a better picture.

Be aware

- Children may be unfamiliar with the idea behind the code-hexagon to represent changes in all directions. If necessary, go through question 1 together.

Outcomes

- I can explore and record patterns in numbers.
- I can recognise general patterns when adding and subtracting.

Challenge Plan: Year 3

A1: comparing 3-digit numbers; partitioning 3-digit numbers; counting objects by grouping; counting on and back in 100s

Summary

Y3 A1.2

Making moves

A small group working with an adult

Year 3 Challenge PCMs 3 and 4

Calculators (optional); chess pieces (optional)

Abacus Evolve objectives

- **Y4** Add or subtract 1, 10, 100 or 1000 to or from any integer
- **Y4** Add several multiples of 10 or 100
- **Y4** Add and subtract 2- and 3-digit multiples of 10

Framework objectives

- **Y4** Partition, round and order four-digit whole numbers; use positive and negative numbers in context and position them on a number line; state inequalities using the symbols $<$ and $>$ (e.g. $^-3 > ^-5$, $^-1 < ^+1$)
- **Y4** Use knowledge of addition and subtraction facts and place value to derive sums and differences of pairs of multiples of 10, 100 or 1000
- **Y4** Solve one-step and two-step problems involving numbers, money or measures, including time; choose and carry out appropriate calculations, using calculator methods where appropriate

Teacher notes

Preparation
Photocopy PCMs 3 and 4, one copy of each per child. If you can find some chess pieces, this would be helpful.

Activity
- Discuss chess pieces and how they move on a chessboard. Explain the different ways in which pawns, rooks, knights, bishops, queens and kings move. *In this activity, moves will be made on number squares instead of a chessboard. The pieces can start on any of the four sides of the square.*
- Start by using the 1 to 100 square on PCM 3. Remind children that pawns can start by moving one or two spaces forward. So their moves could result in a change of $^+10$ or $^+20$ on the board.
- Next look at how kings can move: just one space, but in any direction, including diagonally. *What number changes could one move make?* ($^+1$, $^-1$, $^+10$, $^-10$, $^+9$, $^-9$, $^+11$, $^-11$)
- Ask the group to investigate what changes to a starting number the other pieces' moves can cause. Suggest that they work up through the pieces from rook to bishop to queen, leaving the knight to the end.
- Ask children to explore the same moves on the 101 to 200 square (PCM 3) and the 5 to 500 square (PCM 4). *What happens now when pieces move? How is this different from on the previous number square?*

Further extension
- Help children to explore a knight's moves on the 110 to 900 square (PCM 4). Ask them to start from 120 and reach 430 using knight's moves. *Add all the numbers in the squares that the knight moves to, except the start and finish squares. What does this journey total? Can you find a journey that makes 590?*
- Suggest that they now make up their own knight's journeys and find the totals. They can then pass each other the start and finish squares and a journey target number, as a problem to solve. They could include journeys from one of the centre numbers to one of the corner numbers.

Be aware

- Children may have greatly different prior knowledge of chess and chess moves. Be aware that children who have little prior knowledge may need support.

Outcomes

- I can solve number problems by using the patterns on number squares.
- I can try different options and decide which is best.

Supporting resources

There is another chess-related number problem here:
- http://nrich.maths.org/public/viewer.php?obj_id=1317

A1: comparing 3-digit numbers; partitioning 3-digit numbers; counting objects by grouping; counting on and back in 100s

Summary

Y3 A1.3

Make a number

Individuals, pairs or groups working independently

Year 3 Challenge Textbook page 4

Year 3 Challenge PCM 5

Abacus Evolve objectives

- Know what each digit in a 3-digit number represents, including 0 as a place holder
- Rehearse pairs of multiples of 10 that total 100
- Derive all pairs of multiples of 5 that total 100

Framework objectives

- *Partition three-digit numbers into multiples of 100, 10 and 1 in different ways*
- *Derive and recall all addition and subtraction facts for each number to 20, sums and differences of multiples of 10 and number pairs that total 100*
- Identify patterns and relationships involving numbers or shapes, and use these to solve problems

Teacher notes

Preparation
Photocopy PCM 5, one copy per child. You may also want to have a couple of spares.

Getting started
Show children the patterns on Textbook page 4 and PCM 5, and make sure they understand the rules set out on the Textbook page.

Activity
- Children work from Textbook page 4. They are shown a pattern made up of triangles, kites and hexagons with numbers written in some of the shapes. They are asked to complete the pattern on PCM 5, following the given rules.
- There are only a few different solutions that satisfy all the rules. However, during their investigations, children will identify other combinations of numbers that meet some, but not all of the criteria (for example, the numbers in the two hexagons do not add to 200 and 300). Such patterns are interesting and valuable stages of the investigation.
- Children can explore the possibilities for filling in the second pattern on the PCM. They can then move on to the third pattern, depending on how confident they are at this stage. All the while they are strengthening the bonds to 100 made from multiples of 5.

Be aware

- The challenge here is related to both number operation and spatial awareness. Children may not be equally able in both areas of maths.

Outcomes

- I can investigate possible sets of numbers to fit a rule.
- I can search for alternative solutions.

Summary

Y3 A1.4

Sheets of stamps

Individuals, pairs or groups working independently

Year 3 Challenge Textbook page 5

Abacus Evolve objectives

- **Y4** Understand multiplication as repeated addition
- **Y4** Rehearse the concept of multiplication as describing an array
- **Y4** Recognise multiples of 2, 3, 4, 5 and 10, up to the tenth multiple
- **Y4** Add and subtract 2- and 3-digit multiples of 10

Framework objectives

- **Y4** *Develop and use written methods to record, support and explain multiplication and division of two-digit numbers by a one-digit number, including division with remainders (e.g. 15 × 9, 98 ÷ 6)*
- **Y4** *Derive and recall multiplication facts up to 10 × 10, the corresponding division facts and multiples of numbers to 10 up to the tenth multiple*
- **Y4** *Use knowledge of addition and subtraction facts and place value to derive sums and differences of pairs of multiples of 10, 100 or 1000*
- **Y4** *Solve one-step and two-step problems involving numbers, money or measures, including time; choose and carry out appropriate calculations, using calculator methods where appropriate*

Teacher notes

Activity

Children work from Textbook page 5. They are shown sheets of stamps worth 5p and 10p, and are asked to work out the total values of a row and a sheet of each type of stamp. They are then shown stamps of other values: 20p, 25p, 50p, £1, £2, £2·50 and £5. They find ways of using a specified number of stamps to make a specified total, using two different stamp values. Children are then asked to find ways to make specified totals using as few stamps as possible. They can use any of the nine stamps shown on the page.

Be aware

- Some children will still be working out multiplications using repeated addition. This activity can be used to help them to start using known multiplication facts and adjusting; the arrays of stamps support this process.

Outcomes

- I can count arrays of 5s, 10s, 20s, 25s, 50s, 100s, 200s, and 500s.
- I can solve problems by combining two patterns and record my solutions.

Summary

Y3 ☆ A1.5

Calculator rules

A small group working with an adult

Year 3 Challenge Textbook page 6

Calculators; strips of paper

Abacus Evolve objectives

- **Y4** Count on and back in 25s or 50s to and from 1000
- **Y4** Use a calculator to carry out one- and two-step calculations involving all four operations; recognise negative numbers in the display, correct mistaken entries and interpret the display correctly in the context of money

Framework objectives

- **Y4** Derive and recall multiplication facts up to 10 × 10, the correspoding division facts and multiples of numbers to 10 up to the tenth multiple
- **Y4** Use a calculator to carry out one-step and two-step calculations involving all four operations; recognise negative numbers in the display, correct mistaken entries and interpret the display correctly in the context of money

Teacher notes

Preparation
Check how your calculators produce a constant function. For some calculators this is: 5 + + 4 = = = …

Getting started
Establish the way your calculators can be set up to produce a constant function. If it is different from the method shown on the Textbook page, explain this to children.

Activity
- Children work from Textbook page 6. They practise using the constant function on their calculators by starting at one number and reaching another one in steps of a specified size. Children then have a go at creating their own 'stepping problems' to give to a partner to try out.
- Next, children try typing a 4-digit number into their calculators, and repeatedly subtracting 100 until there is a 0 in the hundreds place.
- Children solve a problem involving transporting a class of children on a school trip using coaches that have different maximum capacities. They should continue to use the constant function, rather than the multiplication or division buttons.
- Lastly, children try using calculators to run through multiplication tables by using repeated addition.

If you have time
Introduce the game of 'calculator aliens'. This involves two players and one calculator. Children type a 4- or 5-digit number into the calculator. They take turns to 'zap' a digit called by the other player. For example, if the number is 34 567 and Player 1 calls *Zap the four*, Player 2 presses '– 4 0 0 0'.

Be aware

- Children may not recognise the need to record their workings, and so 'lose' their work; some may need special paper with a line of calculator button shapes within which to record each button press.

Outcomes

- I can make a calculator count in steps of any number.
- I can understand the patterns that result from a calculator's constant function.

Supporting resources

Look here for more activities involving the constant function on a calculator:
- http://www.blackdouglas.com.au/resorce/cal_act/confunc.htm
There are some more activities involving calculators, here:
- www.dete.sa.gov.au/limestonecoast/files/pages/new%20page/T_D/Michael%20Ymer/Calculator_games_and_activ.doc

Challenge Plan: Year 3

A1: comparing 3-digit numbers; partitioning 3-digit numbers; counting objects by grouping; counting on and back in 100s

Summary

Y3 A1.6

Egyptian numbers

Pairs or groups working independently

Year 3 Challenge Textbook page 7

Internet

Abacus Evolve objectives

- Say the number that is 1, 10 or 100 more or less than a given number
- Partition 3-digit numbers into H, T and U
- Know what each digit in a 3-digit number represents, including 0 as a place holder

Framework objectives

- Read, write and order whole numbers to at least 1000 and position them on a number line; count on from and back to zero in single-digit steps or multiples of 10
- *Partition three-digit numbers into multiples of 100, 10 and 1 in different ways*

Teacher notes

Preparation
Check the weblinks below to ensure that they remain active and appropriate.

Activity
Children work from Textbook page 7. They read about the ancient Egyptian system of hieroglyphs and are shown pictures of the seven hieroglyphs used to represent the numbers 1, 10, 100, 1000, 10 000, 100 000 and 1 000 000. They are also shown two ways in which the ancient Egyptians combined these hieroglyphs to represent numbers such as 4622. Children then write some numbers using hieroglyphs.

Information
As the hieroglyphs use different pictures to represent tens, hundreds, thousands, and so on, it was not necessary for them to have a symbol for zero.

Be aware

- The non-place value system used is likely to be unfamiliar to children, and could be difficult, but will throw more light on our place value system.

Outcomes

- I can read and write numbers up to millions in Egyptian hieroglyphs.
- I can read numbers written in hieroglyphs.

Supporting resources

You can find further information on the ancient Egyptian number system here:
- http://www.eyelid.co.uk/numbers.htm
- http://forestpath.net/egypt/maths/
There is further information about the Eye of Horus here:
- http://mathworld.wolfram.com/EyeofHorusFraction.html

Challenge Plan: Year 3

B1: addition and subtraction facts; adding numbers by finding pairs; classifying and describing 2D shapes; lines of symmetry

Summary

Y3 ⬡ B1.1

Circular counting stick

Pairs or groups working independently

Year 3 Challenge Textbook page 8

Year 3 Challenge PCM 6

Counting stick

Abacus Evolve objectives

- Know by heart the multiplication facts for the 5 and 10 times-tables
- Know by heart the multiplication facts for the 3 times-table
- Know by heart the multiplication facts for the 4 times-table
- Begin to know multiplication facts for the 6 times-table and corresponding division facts
- Understand multiplication/division as repeated addition/subtraction
- Extend use of patterns of similar calculations

Framework objectives

- Derive and recall multiplication facts for the 2, 3, 4, 5, 6 and 10 times-tables and the corresponding division facts; recognise multiples of 2, 5 or 10 up to 1000
- Identify patterns and relationships involving numbers or shapes, and use these to solve problems

Teacher notes

Preparation
Photocopy PCM 6, one copy per child. If one enlarged version of the circular counting stick image can be made, this will assist children.

Getting started
First use the familiar (non-circular) counting stick to rehearse some table patterns, inviting children in the group to choose the tables. Then use Textbook page 8 to introduce the circular version of the counting stick. Use the stick to rehearse the ×4 and ×7 tables, continuing around the circle a second time. If possible, allow children to take turns with a large version of the circular stick, before asking them to choose more tables to rehearse.

Activity
Children work from Textbook page 8. They explore times-table patterns further using the image of a circular counting stick. They record their work on PCM 6. Children describe the patterns they notice.

Be aware

- Children may not recognise that each point 'stands for' a whole sequence of numbers such as 4, 14, 24, … and not just a single value.

Outcomes

- I can explore and record patterns in times-tables.
- I can explore multiples beyond the tenth multiple.

Supporting resources

For similar activities see *Notes on Mathematics for Children*, published by ATM:
- http://www.atm.org.uk/buyonline

Challenge Plan: Year 3

B1: addition and subtraction facts; adding numbers by finding pairs; classifying and describing 2D shapes; lines of symmetry

Summary

Y3 ☆ B1.2   **Rows of houses**

Individuals, pairs or groups working independently

Year 3 Challenge Textbook page 9

Year 3 Challenge PCM 7

Calculators; sticky tape or glue

Abacus Evolve objectives

- Know by heart addition and subtraction facts for pairs of numbers that total up to 20
- Extend use of patterns of similar calculations

Framework objectives

- *Derive and recall all addition and subtraction facts for each number to 20, sums and differences of multiples of 10 and number pairs that total 100*
- Solve one-step and two-step problems involving numbers, money or measures, including time, choosing and carrying out appropriate calculations

Teacher notes

Preparation
Photocopy PCM 7, one copy per child. You may also wish to have some extras.

Activity
Children work from Textbook page 9. They are introduced to the idea of writing two numbers in the centre of a simple drawing of a house, then finding the sum of the two numbers and writing it on the roof, then finding the difference between the two numbers and writing it on the bottom of the house. Children explore this idea briefly, solving five problems. They are then encouraged to devise similar problems for each other: they should make the numbers as challenging as they can manage.
Children then move on to the idea of a row of houses, with the sum and difference transferring to the centre of the next house in the row. Children complete an initial row of five houses, which has a checking number already in place in the final house. They then explore this idea further by choosing their own starting numbers.

Extra help
Children should notice that the numbers double in every other house. They can use this to help check their working.

Further extension
If the roof of a fourth house is 100, what could the rest of the numbers in the row be? Each child makes a row of four houses to explore this. Children then share and discuss their answers in the group.

If you have time
Children can discuss if the numbers always double in every other house. *Why might that be?*

Be aware

- Children are likely to notice the doubling property of alternate houses in a row, but are unlikely to be able to see why this happens at this stage.

Outcomes

- I can solve number problems.
- I can pose good number problems.
- I can follow a rule and continue a pattern of numbers.

Challenge Plan: Year 3

B1: addition and subtraction facts; adding numbers by finding pairs; classifying and describing 2D shapes; lines of symmetry

Summary

Y3 ◯ B1.3

Magic squares

A small group working with an adult

Year 3 Challenge PCMs 8 and 9

Digit cards 1–9; 3 by 3 square grids

Abacus Evolve objectives

- **Y4** Add several 1-digit numbers
- **Y4** Add by finding pairs that total 9, 10 or 11
- **Y4** Recognise and explain patterns and relationships, generalise and predict

Framework objectives

- **Y4** Use knowledge of addition and subtraction facts and place value to derive sums and differences of pairs of multiples of 10, 100 or 1000
- **Y4** Report solutions to puzzles and problems, giving explanations and reasoning orally and in writing, using diagrams and symbols
- **Y4** Respond appropriately to the contributions of others in the light of alternative view points

Teacher notes

Preparation
Photocopy PCMs 8 and 9, two or three copies of each per group.

Getting started
Make sure each child has a set of digit cards 1–9 and a 3 by 3 square grid, ideally one that is large enough to use with the digit cards.

Activity
- Ask children to arrange their digit cards in their 3 by 3 grid. They find the total of each row and each column, recording these to the right and below the grid. These six totals will generally vary considerably.
- Give children PCM 8. They try to write the numbers 1–9 in the first 3 by 3 grid so that each column and row has the same total (15). Encourage children to discuss this as a group.
- Ask children to use the other grids on PCM 8 to find different arrangements of the nine digits that give the same total in each row and column. Encourage children to discuss what they have found. *Are the totals always 15? How many different squares have you found? Are any of the squares really the same, but rotated or flipped?* (In fact there are nine essentially different solutions, each of which can be rotated or reflected to produce eight variants, giving 72 different squares in total.)
- Give children PCM 9. This part of the activity involves pairs of magic squares, where the first is transformed into the second by applying a rule. Children first complete the example, adding 10 to each number in the grid, then find the new totals, discussing how and why they have changed. Children then create their own rules and transform some of the squares they created during the first half of the activity. The group discuss the outcomes of this, checking each other's working.

Extra help
Children can start by exploring ways to make 15 with three digit cards. They note down ways to make 15, then try to arrange them into columns and rows in a 3 by 3 square.

Further extension
Children write numbers 1–9 in a 3 by 3 grid and write the totals (the totals should not all be the same). They copy their grid onto another piece of paper, but only write the totals. They then give this to another child, and challenge them to work out where the numbers 1–9 must go, in order to make the given totals.

If you have time
This activity can be varied using other sets of numbers (other than 1–9) on the same grid.

Be aware

- If children are struggling to make the rows/columns total 15, get them started by telling them that the central number must be 5.

Outcomes

- I can create magic squares.
- I can pose good problems about number squares.

Challenge Plan: Year 3

B1: addition and subtraction facts; adding numbers by finding pairs; classifying and describing 2D shapes; lines of symmetry

Summary

Y3 ○ B1.4

Tetrominoes

A small group working with an adult

Year 3 Challenge Textbook page 10

Identical squares; square dot grid paper; identical equilateral triangles (optional); triangular dot grid paper (optional)

Abacus Evolve objectives

- Classify and describe 2D shapes, including quadrilaterals
- Identify right angles in 2D shapes and the environment

Framework objectives

- Relate 2D shapes and 3D solids to drawings of them; describe, visualise, classify, draw and make the shapes
- Identify patterns and relationships involving numbers or shapes, and use these to solve problems
- Sustain conversation, explaining or giving reasons for their views or choices

Teacher notes

Preparation
Children need identically-sized squares and equilateral triangles for exploration purposes and square dot grid paper and triangular dot grid paper for recording.

Getting started
Set out the squares and the square dot grid paper on the table and explain that they will help children with their exploration.

Activity
- Look at Textbook page 10 together. Read the information about dominoes, trominoes and tetrominoes, and discuss as a group. Make sure children are comfortable with the idea that the two dominoes shown are the same.
- Challenge children to find all of the possible tetrominoes (there are five). They can use squares for this, or draw sketches. Once children think they have found them all, they should draw them carefully on square dot grid paper and cut them out. *How can you be sure you have found them all?* Look at all the shapes as a group. *Have you all drawn the same shapes?* Discuss any discrepancies and help children to work as a group to decide which ones are the correct five.
- Children then solve two puzzles: fit the five tetrominoes into a 5 by 5 square with one domino gap and one tromino gap; fit the five tetrominoes into a 4 by 6 rectangle with two domino gaps.
- Ask the group to gather together all their tetrominoes and sort them into the different shapes. They discard the squares and rectangles. Each pair then chooses one of the remaining shapes, and takes as many copies of their chosen shape as possible. Pairs then try to fit their shape together in a pattern that could continue indefinitely, without gaps. They record this tessellation pattern on square dot grid paper. Look at all the patterns as a group and discuss.

Extra help
When making tetrominoes, children can start by looking at different ways of adding a square to the two trominoes.

Further extension
As a group children can discuss the patterns they have produced. *How are they different? How are they similar or the same?*

If you have time
Children can move on to look at pentiamonds (made from five equilateral triangles).

Be aware

- Children may find the idea that there are only five tetrominoes difficult. They should be aware that reflections and rotations do not count as new shapes. Help them to work out a methodical system for finding all the possibilities to confirm that they have exhausted all the options.
- Children may need some help with cutting out their tetrominoes carefully and accurately.

Outcomes

- I can find all the shapes that can be made from four squares.
- I can solve puzzles and problems with shapes.

Challenge Plan: Year 3

B1: addition and subtraction facts; adding numbers by finding pairs; classifying and describing 2D shapes; lines of symmetry

Summary

Y3 B1.5

Tile patterns

Individuals, pairs or groups working independently

Year 3 Challenge Textbook page 11

Year 3 Challenge PCM 10

Square dot paper

Abacus Evolve objectives

- **Y4** Rehearse the concept of line symmetry
- **Y4** Sketch the reflection of a shape in a mirror line parallel to one side
- **Y4** Describe and visualise 2D shapes
- **Y4** Recognise and explain patterns and relationships, generalise and predict

Framework objectives

- **Y4** Draw polygons and classify them by identifying their properties, including their line symmetry
- **Y4** Identify and use patterns, relationships and properties of numbers or shapes; investigate a statement involving numbers and test it with examples

Teacher notes

Preparation
Photocopy PCM 10 onto card, two copies per group. Cut out the tiles and the 2 by 2 squares.

Activity
Children work from Textbook page 11. Each child or pair chooses one of the tiles from PCM 10 and arranges four copies of it in a 2 by 2 square. They investigate how many different patterns they can make in this way, and draw each one on square dot paper.
They can discuss their findings as a group, and think about whether all the tiles have the same number of possible arrangements.
Children are then introduced to the idea of creating a frieze pattern using one of the tiles. They look at an example on the Textbook page and consider possible rules to describe how the tile is repositioned as it moves along the frieze. They then choose their own tile and make up a rule, then produce and record their own frieze patterns.

Extra help
If children are having trouble finding all the 2 by 2 square patterns, they can try describing the shape that they see at the centre of each pattern (e.g. *it looks like a star*). This should distinguish patterns and help avoid confusion.

Information
Tiles can be moved in three different ways: they can be translated (slid along) rotated (through a $\frac{1}{4}$ turn, $\frac{1}{2}$ turn or $\frac{3}{4}$ turn) or reflected (in an imagined line of symmetry at right angles to the frieze). Notice that for some tiles reflection produces a second version of the tile, whereas for others the original and the reflection are identical.

Be aware

- Children may find it difficult to tell whether all the possible 2 by 2 arrangements for a tile have been found. They may find it helpful to colour the tiles or focus on the central shape in each arrangement.

Outcomes

- I can find all the possible ways to arrange four tiles in a square.
- I can make a frieze pattern from a tile design.
- I can describe the rules behind a pattern of tiles.

Challenge Plan: Year 3

B1: addition and subtraction facts; adding numbers by finding pairs; classifying and describing 2D shapes; lines of symmetry

Summary

Y3 ⬡ B1.6

M C Escher

Pairs or groups working independently

Year 3 Challenge Textbook page 12

Paper squares; paper equilateral triangles (optional)

Abacus Evolve objectives

- Identify and sketch lines of symmetry in simple shapes
- Sketch the reflection of a simple shape in a mirror line along one edge
- Recognise shapes with no lines of symmetry

Framework objectives

- Draw and complete shapes with reflective symmetry; draw the reflection of a shape in a mirror line along one side

Teacher notes

Getting started
Make sure that children understand the concept of tessellation.

Activity
Children work from Textbook page 12. They read about M C Escher and find out about some of his work involving tessellation. They are introduced to the method he used to transform simple tessellations into imaginative tessellations. The method is often called 'put and take' (although it should really be 'take and put'!).
Children work in pairs to explore this method of transforming a square for themselves. They should find it easy to produce shapes that will tessellate, but are more interesting. As a group, children discuss how the shapes fit together. This should lead them towards talking about translation (although they are unlikely to use this word).
Children then go on to choose a different shape to transform using the 'put and take' method.

Further extension
Many of Escher's tessellations are based on equilateral triangles. Ask children to explore using 'put and take' with an equilateral triangle.

If you have time
Start with an Escher tessellation. Ask children to 'undo' it and work out which 'put and take' moves were used to make it.

Be aware

- It is important that the shape taken from one side of the square is replaced on the opposite side. This becomes more difficult as the shape becomes more complex and the original square less obvious.

Outcomes

- I can transform a square into another shape that will tessellate.
- I can research more about Escher's tessellations.

Supporting resources

Escher-type tessellations can be constructed online at:
- http://gwydir.demon.co.uk/jo/tess/sqtile.htm

Challenge Plan: Year 3

C1: lengths in metres and centimetres; decimal notation for metres and centimetres; lists, tally charts and frequency tables; pictograms

Summary

Y3 ☆ C1.1

Estimating measurements

A small group working with an adult

Year 3 Challenge PCM 11

Length-measuring equipment

Abacus Evolve objectives

- Measure and compare lengths using standard units: metres, centimetres
- Use decimal notation for metres and centimetres
- Use a ruler to draw and measure lines to the nearest half centimetre

Framework objectives

- Know the relationships between kilometres and metres, metres and centimetres, kilograms and grams, litres and millilitres; choose and use appropriate units to estimate, measure and record measurements
- *Read, to the nearest division and half-division, scales that are numbered or partially numbered; use the information to measure and draw to a suitable degree of accuracy*

Teacher notes

Preparation
Photocopy PCM 11, several copies for the group.
Gather as many different length-measuring devices as you can. Include measure-transferring devices such as string and strips of card and paper. Identify everyday objects in the classroom, such as packaging items, for children to measure; alternatively ask children to each bring in a suitable object, without revealing why.
Take an accurate measure of one item (e.g. your own height) for modelling purposes.

Activity
- Model the game using the measurement you obtained earlier (your own height). *We are going to estimate my height!* Explain that no estimate can be totally accurate. (At this point you might like to introduce the symbol ≈ for 'is approximately equal to'.) However, if they estimate that your height is between two measurements, they could be correct. The group then discuss, either together or in pairs, what their 'between' estimates will be. No measuring is allowed at this point! Show children how to enter their estimates on a copy of PCM 11. They should each calculate the difference between the two measurements that make up their estimate. Finally, reveal whether anyone has captured your height within their estimates. Children who estimated the range correctly are marked as 'in'; children who did not are marked as 'out'. Compare the successful estimates, explaining that the winner is the child whose estimate has the smallest difference.
- Children then explore further by playing the game several times, taking turns to select a measurable object from the classroom or from amongst the objects they have brought in.

Further extension
Draw children's attention to a circular object, such as the classroom clock, and introduce the word *circumference*. Challenge children to estimate the circumference: they are likely to greatly underestimate its length. Point out how deceptive curved and circular objects are and suggest that children play the game with other circular objects to see if they can get better at estimating circumferences. Children may see that the circumference is 'about three times as long' as the width (diameter).

Be aware

- Children may find the fact that estimating measures cannot be exact a challenging idea.

Outcomes

- I can estimate and measure the lengths of objects.
- I understand that estimating is always approximate.

Supporting resources

A range of resources that give practice in measuring lengths can be found at:
- http://www.primaryresources.co.uk/maths/mathsE1.htm length

Challenge Plan: Year 3

C1: lengths in metres and centimetres; decimal notation for metres and centimetres; lists, tally charts and frequency tables; pictograms

Summary

Y3 ◇ C1.2

Body measures

Pairs and groups working independently

Year 3 Challenge Textbook page 13

Card strips; metre rules; string

Abacus Evolve objectives

- **Y4** Use, read and write standard metric units of length: mm, cm, m, km
- **Y4** Suggest suitable units and measuring equipment to estimate or measure length

Framework objectives

- **Y4** *Choose and use standard metric units and their abbreviations when estimating, measuring and recording length, weight and capacity; know the meaning of 'kilo', 'centi' and 'milli' and, where appropriate, use decimal notation to record measurements (e.g. 1.3 m or 0.6 kg)*
- **Y4** Suggest a line of enquiry and the strategy needed to follow it; collect, organise and interpret selected information to find answers

Teacher notes

Preparation
If using Abacus Evolve, this activity can be used to extend the whole-class investigation.

Getting started
Make sure children understand the meaning of the word *circumference*. Point this word out to them on the Textbook page. Show them how to measure the circumference of their heads using strips of card.

Activity
Children work from Textbook page 13. They measure and compare their head circumference and arm length, recording each pair of measurements in a table and finding the difference between each pair. They then discuss their data, and suggest other pairs of body lengths to compare.
Children then compare their height and arm span (the distance between fingertips when both arms and hands are outstretched). For many adults, there is a surprisingly close link between these two measures. Children, however, may find that one or other measure is significantly longer, since they are still growing. There is an opportunity here to discuss mammals whose measures are very different (for example, orangutans have a much wider stretch than their heights). Children then measure and compare their hand span (the distance between the tips of the thumb and little finger when the hand is outstretched) and foot length. In ancient Egypt, adult hand spans and feet were part of their measuring system, with hand span being set at $\frac{3}{4}$ of a foot. Children look at their data to see whether their measurements have a similar relationship.

Extra help
Children may need some help to recognise the close relationship between pairs of measures. Together discuss the difference between pairs of measures and encourage children to see how relatively small the differences are.

Information
The idea of exploring a correlation between paired data is used only informally in this activity.

Be aware

- Children may be sensitive about body measures. Take any opportunity to stress the positive nature of variations in human body shapes and sizes.

Outcomes

- I can measure body lengths.
- I can look for relationships in pairs of measurements.

Supporting resources

A range of resources that give practice in measuring lengths can be found at:
- http://www.primaryresources.co.uk/maths/mathsE1.htm length

Challenge Plan: Year 3

C1: lengths in metres and centimetres; decimal notation for metres and centimetres; lists, tally charts and frequency tables; pictograms

Summary

Y3 ○ **C1.3**

Making journeys

Individuals, pairs or groups working independently

Year 3 Challenge Textbook page 14

Year 3 Challenge PCM 12

Abacus Evolve objectives

- Know the relationship between kilometres and metres, metres and centimetres
- Use decimal notation for metres and centimetres

Framework objectives

- Know the relationships between kilometres and metres, metres and centimetres, kilograms and grams, litres and millilitres; choose and use appropriate units to estimate, measure and record measurements
- Solve one-step and two-step problems involving numbers, money or measures, including time, choosing and carrying out appropriate calculations

Teacher notes

Preparation
Photocopy PCM 12, one copy per child or pair.

Getting started
Show children the two maps of the Isle of Wight. Discuss how the planning map relates to and simplifies the normal map. Children may need reminding of the link between metres and kilometres.

Activity
Children work from Textbook page 14, using the maps on PCM 12, and the table of distances which combines kilometres and hundreds of metres. They compare the total distances travelled when calculated using the two sources of information.
They then design another trip around the island and again compare the two ways of finding the distance travelled. This prepares the way for later work on the approximate nature of measures and different levels of accuracy.

Extra help
When dividing numbers of kilometres by 1.61, children may need help dealing with decimal places. Discuss rounding, for example 30 km ÷ 1.61 = 18·633540 miles. This can be rounded to 18·5 miles, which is very close and is an easier number.

Further extension
Show children this information: 1 mile = 1·61 kilometres. Explain how to convert kilometres to miles using a calculator: divide the number of kilometres by 1.61. Challenge them to convert the 15 distances in the table on the Textbook page to miles. Remind them that they should first convert the distances to kilometres using decimal notation.

If you have time
Ask children to convert the distances in the table to kilometres using decimal notation.
Ask children to compare the distances on the map with those in the table, and explain why a value such as 23 km 700 m becomes 24 km, while 9 km 300 m becomes 9 km.

Be aware

- Children may be unfamiliar with topological maps like the planner provided on the Textbook page, and may need peer support to familiarise themselves with the idea.

Outcomes

- I can use journey planning maps in kilometres.
- I can use tables of distances in kilometres and metres.
- I can calculate distances for journeys.

Challenge Plan: Year 3

C1: lengths in metres and centimetres; decimal notation for metres and centimetres; lists, tally charts and frequency tables; pictograms

Summary

Y3 C1.4

Designing a survey

A small group working with an adult

Year 3 Challenge Textbook page 15

Abacus Evolve objectives

- Solve a given problem by organising and interpreting numerical data in simple lists, tally charts and frequency tables
- Solve a given problem by organising and interpreting data in pictograms (symbol representing two units)
- Organise and interpret numerical data in bar charts

Framework objectives

- Answer a question by collecting, organising and interpreting data; use tally charts, frequency tables, pictograms and bar charts to represent results and illustrate observations; use ICT to create a simple bar chart
- Follow a line of enquiry by deciding what information is important; make and use lists, tables and graphs to organise and interpret the information
- Explain a process or present information, ensuring items are clearly sequenced, relevant details are included and accounts ended effectively

Teacher notes

Preparation

Prepare a simple general-purpose data collection sheet for the children's surveys.
Have several possible focuses for a survey ready in case children are not able to suggest one.

Activity

- Discuss surveys. *Why might you carry out a survey? What sorts of information could you find out? How would you collect the information? What would you do with the information then?*
- Show children the five steps in carrying out a survey shown on Textbook page 15. The purpose of this example is to help children appreciate the data-handling cycle. Lead them through it, identifying the stages in the process.
- Ask children questions to help them to interpret the bar chart and pictogram. For example: *What make of car was least popular? How many families had a Renault? Which was more popular: Fiat or Peugeot? How many cars were included in the survey?*
- *Are there any questions that can't be answered by looking at these graphs?* Take suggestions, for example *What engine size is most popular? What colour is most popular?*
- Children carry out their own survey, following the five steps described on the Textbook page. Check that the surveys they choose are suitable and can be done within the time available.

Extra help

Ask children to work together as a group to choose a single idea for a survey, to be carried out by the whole group. Children can then gather data between them and work together to go through the five steps.

Further extension

Ask children to present their data in at least two different ways, e.g. pictogram and frequency table. *Which format is more useful when answering questions about the data?* Ask them to explain to the group which format is more useful, and why. *Are there sets of data for which the other format may be more useful?*

Be aware

- Allowing children to use data-handling software is likely to take up a lot of time unless children have some previous experience using this sort of software.

Outcomes

- I can help to design and carry out a survey.
- I can organise and present the survey data.
- I can interpret the data from a survey.

Challenge Plan: Year 3

C1: lengths in metres and centimetres; decimal notation for metres and centimetres; lists, tally charts and frequency tables; pictograms

Summary

Y3 ☆ C1.5   **Stem-and-leaf diagrams**

Individuals, pairs or groups working independently

Year 3 Challenge Textbook page 16

Computer and internet (if possible)

Abacus Evolve objectives

• Solve a given problem by organising and interpreting numerical data in simple lists, tally charts and frequency tables

Framework objectives

• Answer a question by collecting, organising and interpreting data; use tally charts, frequency tables, pictograms and bar charts to represent results and illustrate observations; use ICT to create a simple bar chart
• Follow a line of enquiry by deciding what information is important; make and use lists, tables and graphs to organise and interpret the information

Teacher notes

Getting started
Show children the stem-and-leaf diagram on the Textbook page and check that they understand how it works.

Activity
Children work from Textbook page 16. They are introduced to a stem-and-leaf diagram as a way to present raw data. They draw and interpret a stem-and-leaf diagram.

Further extension
Ask children to think of something they could survey that would generate 1- and 2-digit numbers, for example what day in the month children were born. Challenge them to design and carry out their chosen survey, and represent the data using a stem-and-leaf diagram. *Do you think this is the most useful way to show the data? Why? What format might be better?*

If you have time
Children could also look back at data they have previously put into bar charts or pictograms and see how different it looks in a stem-and-leaf diagram.

Information
Stem-and-leaf diagrams were invented in the middle of the 20th century as a means of handling numerical data in a relatively simple and informal way, whilst retaining the actual values.

Be aware

• Stem-and-leaf diagrams are rarely introduced at this stage, but their basis is place value and partitioning numbers, which should be familiar to children.

Outcomes

• I can read the information in a stem-and-leaf diagram.
• I can draw stem-and-leaf diagrams.
• I can think about whether a stem-and-leaf diagram is better than a pictogram or bar chart as a picture of data.

Supporting resources

This site allows stem-and-leaf plotting online:
• http://argyll.epsb.ca/jreed/comphelp/stemleaf.html

Challenge Plan: Year 3

C1: lengths in metres and centimetres; decimal notation for metres and centimetres; lists, tally charts and frequency tables; pictograms

Summary

Y3 ⚙ C1.6

Minibeasts

Pairs working independently

Year 3 Challenge Textbook page 17

Year 3 Challenge PCM 13

Coloured pencils

Abacus Evolve objectives

- **Y4** Rehearse the use of tally charts to record observations
- **Y4** Represent data in frequency tables
- **Y4** Interpret tally charts and frequency tables
- **Y4** Construct and interpret bar graphs with intervals labelled in 2s, 5s, 10s or 20s
- **Y4** Construct and interpret pictograms where the symbol represents 2, 5, 10 or 20 units

Framework objectives

- **Y4** *Answer a question by identifying what data to collect; organise, present, analyse and interpret the data in tables, diagrams, tally charts, pictograms and bar charts, using ICT where appropriate*
- **Y4** Compare the impact of representations where scales have intervals of differing step size

Teacher notes

Preparation
Photocopy PCM 13, one copy per pair.

Activity
Children work from Textbook page 17. They learn how biologists survey populations of insects and other minibeasts. They design a tally chart and then collect data from PCM 13. Children may find it helpful to colour code the different species. They then produce a bar chart or pictogram of the data, choosing a suitable scale (for example, one unit or picture to represent two, three, four or five creatures). Pairs then write some questions that they could ask someone else about the data, then give the questions to another pair to answer.

Further extension
Ask children to make up two sets of data for minibeasts in different fields. They then draw a pictogram to represent the data in each set. One pictogram should use a symbol to represent two units, and the other should use a symbol to represent five units. Children then show their two pictograms to a partner, and pose statements about the relative data, for example: *There are more spiders in set 2. There are the same number of woodlice in both sets. There are more ants in summer.* The other child has to answer *True, False* or *Can't tell.*

If you have time
Children could draw their own field diagrams with minibeasts in some of the squares. Children can then swap diagrams and analyse each other's data. Pairs then compare their two sets of data.

Be aware

- Children may need peer support and adult help in using the scale of one unit or picture to represent up to five creatures.

Outcomes

- I can collect data in a tally chart.
- I can show data in a bar chart or pictogram.

Supporting resources

Children can read about pooters, and find out how to make their own, at:
- http://www.show.me.uk/site/make/Natural-World/ACT59.html

Challenge Plan: Year 3

D1: adding TU + U, HTU + U; subtracting TU − U, HTU − U; reading time to 5 minutes; reading time on analogue and digital clocks

Summary

Y3 ◌ **D1.1**

Disc numbers

Groups working independently

Year 3 Challenge Textbook page 18

Small discs (optional)

Abacus Evolve objectives

- Continue to recognise that addition can be done in any order
- Add a 1-digit number to a 2-digit number, bridging a multiple of 10
- Add a 1-digit number to a 3-digit number, bridging a multiple of 10

Framework objectives

- *Add or subtract mentally combinations of 1- and 2-digit numbers*
- Represent the information in a puzzle or problem using numbers, images or diagrams; use these to find a solution and present it in context, where appropriate using £.p notation or units of measure
- Identify patterns and relationships involving numbers or shapes, and use these to solve problems
- Explain a process or present information, ensuring items are clearly sequenced, relevant details are included and accounts ended effectively

Teacher notes

Preparation
It would be helpful, but not essential, if small discs were provided that can be numbered on both sides.

Getting started
Look at Textbook page 18 with the group. Explain the numbering on both sides of discs, using demonstration discs if these are available.

Activity
Children work from Textbook page 18. They explore the patterns of totals that can arise from two discs numbered on both sides. They attempt to solve harder challenges using larger numbers, then move on to devising their own numbered disc problems.

Extra help
Ask children to make the four totals into two pairs and find the total of each pair. They should find that each pair has the same total.

Further extension
Start with two discs, then add a third disc with numbers on. Children explore all possible totals with three discs.

If you have time
Ask children to find pairs of discs that have just three possible totals. Discuss any patterns in the numbers on these discs.

Information
The smallest and the biggest numbers add to the same total as the two middle numbers (e.g. 10 + 20 = 12 + 18).

Be aware

- Children who do not play this out practically – because they decide they do not need to do so – may not realise that they are excluded from adding the two numbers on either side of the same disc.

Outcomes

- I can explore and record patterns in numbers when solving problems.
- I can recognise general patterns when adding and subtracting numbers.

Challenge Plan: Year 3

D1: adding TU + U, HTU + U; subtracting TU − U, HTU − U; reading time to 5 minutes; reading time on analogue and digital clocks

Summary

Y3 ⬡ D1.2

Boxed number games

Pairs working independently

Year 3 Challenge Textbook page 19

Year 3 Challenge PCM 14

Coloured pens or pencils; calculators (optional)

Abacus Evolve objectives

- Continue to recognise that addition can be done in any order
- Add a 1-digit number to a 2-digit number, bridging a multiple of 10
- Add a 1-digit number to a 3-digit number, bridging a multiple of 10

Framework objectives

- *Add or subtract mentally combinations of one-digit and two-digit numbers*
- Identify patterns and relationships involving numbers or shapes, and use these to solve problems

Teacher notes

Preparation
Photocopy PCM 14, one copy per pair. These could be cut up into six small game boards, so that they can be stuck into exercise books.

Getting started
Discuss with the group how the rules work. Encourage children to play the first game on the blank grid quite fast.

Activity
Children work from Textbook page 19. In pairs, they use the Textbook page and game boards from PCM 14 to play games on boards of square dot grid paper. They take turns to join two dots, trying to enclose squares. The first game is played on a blank board, and the winner is the player who encloses more squares. The other games involve boards with numbers, and children score points to match the numbers in the squares they enclose. The winner is the player with the higher score at the end.
Make calculators available for checking final scores in games where these are close.

If you have time
Children each make a gameboard where the key number is a multiple of 100. They write their 16 numbers out in a random order, then exchange them with a partner. Children then try to make their partner's board. *Are your boards the same?*

Information
Each numbered board comprises rows, columns and corner squares which total the same amount, the 'key number'. For example, each row and column and the four corners of the first board all total 20, so the board is worth 80 altogether. The key numbers of the other boards are 250, 500 and 1000.

Be aware

- Children may vary significantly in their ability in such a game, so pairs may need to swap around to ensure close games.

Outcomes

- I can look for patterns on number squares.
- I can try out different strategies and decide which is better.

Supporting resources

- The book *Mathematical Games* in the series *Mad About Maths* by Adrian and Jeni Pinel is available from www.beam.co.uk and contains more on this game and its variations.

Challenge Plan: Year 3

D1: adding TU + U, HTU + U; subtracting TU − U, HTU − U; reading time to 5 minutes; reading time on analogue and digital clocks

Summary

Y3 ☆ D1.3 **Subtraction cross-number puzzles**

A small group working with an adult

Year 3 Challenge Textbook page 20

Year 3 Challenge PCM 15

Calculators (optional)

Abacus Evolve objectives

- **Y4** Subtract HTU − TU, HTU − HTU using informal written method of complementary addition
- **Y4** Read and write numbers up to 100 000 in figures and words
- **Y4** Know what each digit in a 5-digit number represents

Framework objectives

- **Y4** Refine and use efficient written methods to add and subtract 2- and 3-digit whole numbers and £.p
- **Y4** Partition, round and order 4-digit whole numbers; use positive and negative numbers in context and position them on a number line; state inequalities using the symbols < and >, e.g. $-3 > -5$, $-1 < +1$

Teacher notes

Preparation
Photocopy PCM 15, one copy per child, with a few spares.

Activity
Using the examples on Textbook page 20 for reference, help children understand how to use empty number lines to subtract a single-digit number from a 3-digit number, and a multiple of 10 from a 3-digit number. Children then solve the first six problems.
Children work from Textbook page 20. Introduce the concept of cross-number puzzles, explaining that they are like crosswords but that the answers are numbers rather than words. Children use the clues on the Textbook page and complete the first puzzle on PCM 15. It may help some children to work in pairs or as a group to solve the first puzzle. Children then create clues to match a completed cross-number puzzle. They can work relatively independently, though occasional support and help may be needed. Children may create sufficiently tough cross-number puzzle clues that they require a calculator to solve them.

Extra help
Children can work in pairs or small groups to solve the first puzzle. Encourage them to discuss strategies.

Be aware

- The use of calculators to devise more challenging clues will often stretch children appropriately, but they should not normally be used initially, or to solve clues that have been produced by other children without a calculator.

Outcomes

- I can subtract small numbers and multiples of 10 from a 3-digit number.
- I can solve a cross-number puzzle.
- I can make a cross-number puzzle for others to solve.

Supporting resources

Free cross-number puzzles at various levels can be found at:
- http://www.teach-nology.com/worksheets/math/puzzles/
A cross number puzzle generator is found at:
- http://puzzlepage.blogspot.com/2008/02/crossnumber-puzzle.html
The following site is dedicated to cross-number puzzles:
- http://www.crossnumber.com/

Challenge Plan: Year 3

D1: adding TU + U, HTU + U; subtracting TU − U, HTU − U; reading time to 5 minutes; reading time on analogue and digital clocks

Summary

Y3 ☆ **D1.4**	**Clocks through time**
👥👥	Pairs working independently
📖	Year 3 Challenge Textbook page 21
	Internet

Abacus Evolve objectives

- Read the time to 5 minutes on analogue clocks
- Use units of time and know the relationship between them: days, hours, minutes, seconds

Framework objectives

- Read the time on a 12-hour digital clock and to the nearest 5 minutes on an analogue clock; calculate time intervals and find start or end times for a given time interval
- Explain a process or present information, ensuring items are clearly sequenced, relevant details are included and accounts ended effectively

Teacher notes

Preparation
Use the website links given below and download sufficient information on water clocks and sundials to enable children to research these during the lesson.

Activity
Children work from Textbook page 21. They learn about the history of clock development, from sundials and water clocks (clepsydra) to early mechanical clocks and modern clocks.
Children work out the time shown on early-style clocks where separate faces are used for hours and minutes.
Children then research either sundials or water clocks, discover their advantages and disadvantages, then try to design one of their own.

Be aware

- Children may need help in recognising the time-scales involved, with ancient, middle-ages and relatively recent historical time all in play, in this potted history. Be aware that some websites may be difficult for them to read, but provide useful images.

Outcomes

- I can read times from pairs of clock faces, with hours and minutes separately.
- I can see how sundials and water clocks work.
- I can research and design a sundial or water clock.

Supporting resources

For information about the development of time-keeping devices:
- http://physics.nist.gov/GenInt/Time/early.html
- http://www.arcytech.org/java/clock/index.html

A modern water clock can be viewed at:
- http://www.childrensmuseum.org/themuseum/icons/waterclock.htm

For information on making a sundial:
- http://www.nmm.ac.uk/make-your-own/sundial

For information on making a water clock:
- http://www.planet-science.com/sciteach/index.html?page=/experiment/expts/watching_clock.html

For information on atomic clocks go to:
- http://www.sciencemuseum.org.uk/onlinestuff/stories/atomic_clocks.aspx

Challenge Plan: Year 3

D1: adding TU + U, HTU + U; subtracting TU − U, HTU − U; reading time to 5 minutes; reading time on analogue and digital clocks

Summary

Y3 D1.5

How much time?

A small group working with an adult

Year 3 Challenge PCM 16

Calculators (optional)

Abacus Evolve objectives

- **Y4** Rehearse the use of seconds as a measure of time
- **Y4** Estimate and measure time using seconds, minutes, hours

Framework objectives

- **Y4** Read time to the nearest minute; use am, pm and 12 hour clock notation; choose units of time to measure time intervals; calculate time intervals from clocks and timetables
- **Y4** Respond appropriately to the contributions of others in the light of alternative viewpoints

Teacher notes

Preparation
Photocopy PCM 16 onto thin A4 card. Cut into 24 playing cards. If more than four children will be playing, copy and make two sets of cards.

Activity
- Establish that there are 60 seconds in 1 minute and 60 minutes in 1 hour. Have a brief oral warm-up, converting between seconds and minutes, minutes and hours.
- Give each child or pair of children a sub-set of six cards. (The cards in a sub-set are all labelled A, B, C or D, and each sub-set comprises a complete self-checking loop or chain.) Demonstrate the different question/answer sections on the cards. Children arrange the cards in question/answer order and make a complete chain, with the question on the last card being answered by the answer on the first card.
- Children work together to make a chain using all four sub-sets of cards.
- When all of the group are ready, shuffle the pack of 24 cards together and deal them out to the children. One child plays a card, then play passes to their right. If the next player has a card that answers the question on the first card (regardless of A, B, C or D notation), they play it; if they don't, they 'pass' and play continues to move to the right. Play continues until one player has no cards left and is the winner.
- Note: For best results, the first card to be played should display the answer 80 (there are four of these in the pack).

Extra help
Give children a 2 by 6 question and answer table in which to record their results from the six linking cards. This should help children keep track of the chain of calculations.

Further extension
Using calculators, children can explore the number of seconds in an hour, in a day or in a week.

If you have time
Play the game again to see if children can play it faster. If appropriate, allow a 'play when you can go' rule, instead of taking turns.

X6.

Be...

- Some children may lose trac... ...and answers unless they also re...

Outcomes

- I can complete a chain of calculations involving time.
- I can convert seconds to minutes, and minutes to hours.

Challenge Plan: Year 3

D1: adding TU + U, HTU + U; subtracting TU − U, HTU − U; reading time to 5 minutes; reading time on analogue and digital clocks

Summary

Y3 D1.6 — **Matching times**

Individuals, pairs or groups working independently

Year 3 Challenge Textbook page 22

Year 3 Challenge PCM 17

Abacus Evolve objectives

- Read the time to 5 minutes on analogue and 12-hour digital clocks
- Solve problems involving time: say the number of minutes earlier or later than a given 5-minute time
- Use units of time and know the relationship between them: days, hours, minutes, seconds

Framework objectives

- Read the time on a 12-hour digital clock and to the nearest 5 minutes on an analogue clock; calculate time intervals and find start or end times for a given time interval
- Solve one- and two-step problems involving numbers, money or measures, including time, choosing and carrying out appropriate calculations

Teacher notes

Preparation
Photocopy PCM 17, one copy per child.

Activity
Children work from Textbook page 22. They work out earlier and later times than a given time, then work out the time in the middle of given start and end times. They work with both analogue and digital displays. Children then do an activity on PCM 17 which requires them to match starting times and durations with given new times. The new times may be earlier or later than the start times, so children are asked to record their findings simply, for example: *12:00, 40 minutes later, 12:40*.

Extra help
Give children a 3 by 6 table with the headings *Starting time*, *Duration* and *End time*. Children can use this to record their results from the linking cards. This should help children keep track of the chain of calculations.

Further extension
Challenge children to design a new version of the PCM activity, making up new start and end times, and durations of over an hour.

Be aware

- The recording requirement here is important, as children can lose track of which pairs they have already used, and must also recognise the need to provide evidence of their completion of such exercises.

Outcomes

- I can add and subtract numbers of minutes less than an hour, to find later and earlier times.
- I can solve time problems and record my solutions.

Challenge Plan: Year 3

E1: understanding multiplication and division; 2 times-table; unit fractions; knowing doubles and deriving halves

Summary

Y3 ☆ E1.1   **Linking multiplication and division**

A small group working with an adult

Year 3 Challenge Textbook page 23

Year 3 Challenge PCM 18

Abacus Evolve objectives

- Understand multiplication/division as repeated addition/subtraction
- Understand division as the inverse of multiplication
- Rehearse division as the inverse of multiplication
- Understand multiplication as describing an array

Framework objectives

- Understand that division is the inverse of multiplication and vice versa; use this to derive and record related multiplication and division number sentences
- Derive and recall multiplication facts for the 2, 3, 4, 5, 6 and 10 times-tables and the corresponding division facts; recognise multiples of 2, 5 or 10 up to 1000
- Identify patterns and relationships involving numbers or shapes, and use these to solve problems
- Actively include and respond to all members of the group

Teacher notes

Preparation
Photocopy PCM 18 onto thin card and cut up the cards. If more than four children will be playing, make two sets.

Activity
Have a brief warm-up using multiplication and division in real-life contexts, for example: *How many rows of 6 chairs can you make with 60 chairs? If there were 6 less chairs, how many rows? How many chairs altogether?*
Children work from Textbook page 23. They learn how arrays can be written as related multiplications and divisions.
Give each child or pair of children a sub-set of six cards from PCM 18. (The cards in a sub-set are all labelled A, B, C or D.) Demonstrate the different question/answer sections on the cards. Children arrange the cards in question/answer order and make a complete chain. Children work together to make a chain using all four sub-sets of cards.
When all of the group are ready, shuffle the 24 cards together and deal them out to the children. Any player with a 24 card starts, then play passes to their right. If the next player has a card that answers the question on the first card (regardless of A, B, C or D notation), they play it; if they don't, they 'pass' and play continues to move to the right. Play continues until one player has no cards left and is the winner.

Extra help
Give children a 2 by 6 question and answer table in which to record their results from the linking cards. This should help children keep track of the chain of calculations.

If you have time
Play the game again to see if children can play it faster. If appropriate, allow a 'play when you can go' rule, instead of taking turns.

Be aware

- Children may have a general understanding that multiplication is commutative and that multiplication and division are inverses, but they may not have made connections between specific multiplications and divisions before.

Outcomes

- I can recognise families of multiplications and divisions.
- I can multiply and divide by single-digit numbers in my head.

Challenge Plan: Year 3

E1: understanding multiplication and division; 2 times-table; unit fractions; knowing doubles and deriving halves

Summary

Y3 **E1.2**

Multiplication grids

Groups working independently

Year 3 Challenge Textbook page 24

2 cm² paper; calculators (optional)

Abacus Evolve objectives

- Understand division as the inverse of multiplication
- Know by heart the multiplication facts for the 2 times-table
- Derive division facts corresponding to the 2 times-table
- Know by heart the multiplication facts for the 3 times-table
- Derive division facts corresponding to the 3 times-table
- Know by heart the multiplication facts for the 4 times-table
- Derive division facts corresponding to the 4 times-table
- Know by heart the multiplication facts for the 5 and 10 times-tables
- Derive division facts corresponding to the 5 and 10 times-tables

Framework objectives

- Understand that division is the inverse of multiplication and vice versa; use this to derive and record related multiplication and division number sentences
- Derive and recall multiplication facts for the 2, 3, 4, 5, 6 and 10 times-tables and the corresponding division facts; recognise multiples of 2, 5 or 10 up to 1000
- Identify patterns and relationships involving numbers or shapes, and use these to solve problems

Teacher notes

Activity
Children work from Textbook page 24. They copy and complete multiplication grids of increasing size on squared paper, working out missing products and multipliers. They then create similar puzzles for others to work out the missing numbers.
Encourage children to look for patterns in the placement of the revealed numbers. There are definite patterns to be found for each size of multiplication grid.

Extra help
Children can start by completing a 3 by 3 multiplication grid with three 1-digit numbers along each side, e.g. 3, 5, 7. Show children how to multiply these numbers together to complete the grid.

Further extension
Children could make up more puzzles using bigger numbers, to see if the patterns they have discovered still hold. They could use calculators to work out the products.

Be aware

- Although familiar with a standard multiplication grid, children may not be used to multiplication tables set out in this way, or with the flexible ways of placing varied numbers to be multiplied on each axis.

Outcomes

- I can solve number problems using my knowledge of multiplication tables.
- I can try out different alternatives and decide which is correct.
- I can find and use patterns when making up puzzles.

Challenge Plan: Year 3

E1: understanding multiplication and division; 2 times-table; unit fractions; knowing doubles and deriving halves

Summary

Y3 ◇ E1.3	**Multiplication investigation**
👥	Groups working independently
📖	Year 3 Challenge Textbook page 25
✏️	Digit cards 0–9; calculators (optional)

Abacus Evolve objectives

- **Y4** Know by heart the multiplication facts for the 2, 3, 4, 5 and 10 times-tables
- **Y4** Know the multiplication facts for the 6 times-table, and the corresponding division facts
- **Y4** Begin to know the multiplication facts for the 7 times-table, and the corresponding division facts
- **Y4** Begin to know the multiplication facts for the 8 times-table, and the corresponding division facts
- **Y4** Begin to know the multiplication facts for the 9 times-table, and the corresponding division facts

Framework objectives

- **Y4** *Derive and recall multiplication facts up to 10 × 10, the corresponding division facts and multiples of numbers to 10 up to the tenth multiple*
- **Y4** Represent a puzzle or problem using number sentences, statements or diagrams; use these to solve the problem; present and interpret the solution in the context of the problem
- **Y4** Report solutions to puzzles and problems, giving explanations and reasoning orally and in writing, using diagrams and symbols

Teacher notes

Getting started
Put several sets of digit cards 0–9 on the table.

Activity
Children work from Textbook page 25. Initially they work out answers to four TU × U problems created using a set of four digits. They then use digit cards to work out other possible TU × U calculations that can be made from the same four digits, exploring the different possibilities. They make similar puzzles for a partner to solve.
Children move on to finding the possible combinations three digits in this arrangement: □ × □ + □ = □□

Further extension
Using selected digit cards, children could try to solve problems of the form □□ × □ − □ = □□ For example, the digits 1, 1, 3, 4, 5 and 6 can be arranged to make 13 × 5 − 4 = 61.

Be aware

- Although brackets are implied in this activity, there are no ambiguities because the multiplication is read before the addition, when reading from left to right. Brackets are not formally introduced in Year 3, but children may be introduced to brackets informally within this investigation if they are ready to learn about them.

Outcomes

- I can work out answers to multiplications.
- I can look for other multiplications to find answers.

Summary

Y3 ⭐ **E1.4**

Fraction sentences

A small group working with an adult

Year 3 Challenge Textbook page 26

Digit cards 0–9; linking cubes; plastic or paper coins

Abacus Evolve objectives	Framework objectives
• Recognise unit fractions • Find unit fractions of numbers	• Find unit fractions of numbers and quantities (e.g. $\frac{1}{2}$, $\frac{1}{3}$, $\frac{1}{4}$ and $\frac{1}{6}$ of 12 litres) • Identify patterns and relationships involving numbers or shapes, and use these to solve problems

---

Teacher notes

Getting started
Introduce the group to the unit fraction sentence format shown on Textbook page 26. Show how to use the digit cards to form the sentence: $\frac{1}{2}$ of 10 = 5. Point out that this can also be written as $\frac{1}{2} \times 10 = 5$. Give children cubes and money as practical support.

Activity
Children work from Textbook page 26. There are three stages in the activity. First children use digit cards to complete simple fraction sentences using unit fractions. They should use cubes as practical support if needed. Then they use larger numbers of cubes to build harder unit fraction sentences, and create problems for a partner to solve. They move on to relating 'unit fraction of' to 'divide by' and 'multiply by', for example, $\frac{1}{4}$ of 20 = 5, 20 ÷ 4 = 5, and 5 × 4 = 20. These are illustrated using arrays that can be 'read' in all these different ways.

Further extension
Give children digit cards 0–9. Challenge them to use between four and six of them to make a correct fraction sentence of the form $\frac{\Box}{\Box}$ of $\Box$ = $\Box$ (the second two boxes could stand for 1- or 2-digit numbers). The fractions do not have to be unit fractions. Once children have made a correct sentence, e.g. $\frac{1}{2}$ of 6 = 3, ask them how many different fraction sentences could be made in this way. Encourage them to design a systematic approach to this investigation before starting.

If you have time
Introduce some non-unit fractions. For example, take 12 cubes and ask a child to separate out $\frac{1}{3}$ of them. *How much would two thirds be?* Encourage children to split the remaining eight cubes into two groups of four, and identify that two groups of four is $\frac{2}{3}$ of 12. Now ask children to work in pairs. One child in each pair takes a number of cubes. Their partner gives them a non-unit fraction. The first child must show the given fraction of cubes and say the amount.

Be aware	Outcomes
• Children may see fractions, division and multiplication as separate, and so be resistant to building the connections required here. Some may become temporarily confused before sorting this out and strengthening their understanding.	• I can find unit fractions of numbers of objects. • I understand how unit fractions can be linked to divisions and multiplications.

Challenge Plan: Year 3

E1: understanding multiplication and division; 2 times-table; unit fractions; knowing doubles and deriving halves

Summary

Y3 E1.5

Function machines

A small group working with an adult

Year 3 Challenge PCM 19

Abacus Evolve objectives

- **Y4** Double or halve 2-digit numbers by doubling or halving the tens first
- **Y4** Derive doubles of integers up to 50 and the corresponding halves
- **Y4** Use known number facts and place value to multiply or divide mentally

Framework objectives

- **Y4** Identify the doubles of 2-digit numbers; use these to calculate doubles of multiples of 10 and 100 and derive the corresponding halves
- **Y4** Solve one-step and two-step problems involving numbers, money or measures, including time; choose and carry out appropriate calculations, using calculator methods where appropriate

Teacher notes

Preparation

Photocopy PCM 19, one copy per child, possibly cut into different sections for use in different parts of the lesson.

Activity

- Use the top section of PCM 19 to introduce the concept of function machines, explaining the terms input and output. Ask children to choose some input numbers and find their outputs, then to choose some output numbers and work out the inputs.
- Show children the function machines in the middle section of PCM 19. Explain that these machines can be linked together, so that the output of the first machine goes straight into the second machine. Demonstrate how this works: write a function for the two machines and draw an arrow linking the output of the first machine to the input of the second. Write a small number in the first input box. Ask children for the output. Write it in the output box. *This output number goes straight into the next machine.* Copy the number into the second input box and find the final output. Then put a different output for machine 2, and ask children to work out the input for machine 1. Give children some time to try this out for themselves in pairs.
- Look back at the machines in the top section of PCM 19. *There are three functions here. How many different ways could we link up pairs of machines?* Give children time to discuss this and try it out. (There are six different combinations.) *Does each combination give a different final output?*
- Extend to three machines linked together using these examples:
  - double → halve → add 4 (add 4)
  - add 4 → halve → double (add 4)
  - double → add 4 → halve (add 2)
  - halve → add 4 → double (add 8)
- Consider each example. *Can you find a single machine that could replace the three machines each time?* (Answers are in brackets.) Question children to see if they can say how this works. Extend to more difficult combinations of functions using examples such as: ×4 → +12 → find $\frac{1}{4}$ of, and ×10 → +6 → halve. Children invent their own combinations. If using 'divide by', encourage them to use only 'halve', 'third' and 'quarter'.

Extra help

Model a function machine with the group. Give each child a function, such as 'add 10', or 'double'. Give each child an input number and ask them to use their function to tell you the output number. E.g. the input number is 26, 'add 10', the output number is 36.

Further extension

Children use the bottom section of PCM 19 to explore finding three missing functions for given inputs and outputs.

Be aware

- Children may initially assume that the reverse of a two-step machine such as ×4, +2 will be ÷4, −2. Practical experience initially supported by their group should resolve this.

Outcomes

- I can find the output from a number machine when given the input.
- I can find the input to a number machine when told the output.

Supporting resources

This website offers an animated function machine:
- http://www.bbc.co.uk/schools/ks2bitesize/maths/activities/mentalmaths.shtml

Challenge Plan: Year 3

E1: understanding multiplication and division; 2 times-table; unit fractions; knowing doubles and deriving halves

Summary

Y3 ⭐ E1.6

Doubling and halving shapes

Pairs working independently

Year 3 Challenge Textbook page 27

Year 3 Challenge PCM 20

Abacus Evolve objectives

- Know by heart doubles of numbers up to 20 and the corresponding halves
- Continue to recognise halving as the inverse of doubling
- Classify and describe 2D shapes, including quadrilaterals

Framework objectives

- Use knowledge of number operations and corresponding inverses, including doubling and halving, to estimate and check calculations
- Relate 2D shapes and 3D solids to drawings of them; describe, visualise, classify, draw and make the shapes
- Identify patterns and relationships involving numbers or shapes, and use these to solve problems
- Sustain conversation, explaining or giving reasons for their views or choices

Teacher notes

Preparation
Photocopy PCM 20, at least one copy per pair. The top grid will be needed throughout the lesson, whereas the bottom grid is used only in the Extra activity.

Activity
Children work from Textbook page 27. They work out how to use the first grid on PCM 20 to double and halve the areas of shapes. If necessary, point out that in order to halve a shape, it needs to have an even number of triangles to begin with. They explore this property for various shapes. They also double a shape repeatedly, to produce shapes with ×4 and ×8 the area. Encourage children to understand that the shapes do not change as they grow or get smaller, they are just enlarged (or reduced). Note that the grid forces a rotation as a shape's area is doubled.

If you have time
Give children two clean copies of PCM 20. Ask them to create a small picture by colouring in triangles on the first grid. Then ask them to copy the picture onto the second copy of the PCM, but make it double the size.

Be aware

- The activity links doubling and halving with spatial awareness. This application of doubling and halving to a broader context can prove challenging even when children are strong in the separate topics.

Outcomes

- I can enlarge shapes so that the area is doubled but the shape remains the same.
- I can reverse this to halve the area of shapes.

Summary

Y3 A2.1

Rounding

Individuals, pairs or groups working independently

 Year 3 Challenge Textbook page 28

Abacus Evolve objectives

- Round numbers less than 100 to the nearest 10
- Begin to round 3-digit numbers to the nearest 100 and 10
- Understand division as grouping
- Round up or down after division, depending on the context
- Understand and use £.p notation
- Solve 'real-life' problems involving money (comparing amounts)

Framework objectives

- Round 2- or 3-digit numbers to the nearest 10 or 100 and give estimates for their sums and differences
- Use practical and informal written methods to multiply and divide 2-digit numbers (e.g. 13 × 3, 30 ÷ 4); round remainders up or down, depending on the context
- Solve one-step and two-step problems involving numbers, money or measures, including time, choosing and carrying out appropriate calculations

Teacher notes

Getting started

Introduce the concept of rounding numbers to the nearest 10 and 100 and to the nearest 50 and 500. Discuss situations where different degrees of accuracy could be quite significant (e.g. rounding a length of pipe to the nearest metre might be acceptable when buying materials from a hardware store, but rounding measurements to the nearest metre would be disastrous for a rocket designer). *How do we know when to round up and when to round down?*

Activity

Children work from Textbook page 28. They answer questions about rounding in three different contexts:
- rounding to the nearest specified number (10, 100, 500, 1000)
- rounding up or down after a division, depending on context
- given a round number, working out the highest and lowest possible numbers that can be rounded to give that number.

Extra help

Encourage children to use an empty number line for visual support. This should help them to work out what the nearest 10, 100, etc. might be, and also help them to work out the highest and lowest possible numbers.

Be aware

- Children may find it challenging to divide larger numbers. Allow them to use a calculator if necessary.
- Finding the highest and lowest possible numbers that round to given numbers can be tricky. Discussing with their group should help them.

Outcomes

- I can round numbers and amounts of money to the nearest 10, 50, 100, 500 and 1000.
- I can decide whether I should round up or down.
- I can work out divisions by grouping.

Supporting resources

Children can practise rounding numbers up to 1 000 000 using the online activity at:
- http://www.aplusmath.com/Flashcards/rounding.html
They could also try this helipad rounding game:
- http://www.ictgames.com/helipad%20hops7.html

Summary

Y3 ⬠ **A2.2**

Ordering numbers

 A small group working with an adult

 Year 3 Challenge Textbook page 29

Year 3 Challenge PCM 21

 Calculators (optional)

Abacus Evolve objectives

- **Y4** Know what each digit in a 5-digit number represents
- **Y4** Recognise the relationship between Th, H, T and U
- **Y4** Say one or more numbers lying between two given numbers
- **Y4** Compare and order numbers up to 10 000

Framework objectives

- **Y4** Partition, round and order four-digit whole numbers; use positive and negative numbers in context and position them on a number line; state inequalities using the symbols < and >, e.g. ⁻3 > ⁻5, ⁻1 < ⁺1
- **Y4** Take different roles in groups and use the language appropriate to them, including roles of leader, reporter, scribe and mentor

Teacher notes

Preparation
Photocopy PCM 21 onto card and cut up the cards. If more than four children will be playing, make two sets.

Activity
- Lead a brief warm-up, involving ordering 2- and 3-digit numbers and amounts of money.
- Children work from Textbook page 29. First they are asked to identify the smallest and largest numbers from a set of numbers, then to order them. Then they move on to finding a number between two numbers, before finding the number exactly half-way between two numbers. If children are struggling with finding half-way numbers, ask a child who does understand to explain to the group. If they are all struggling, explain that they first need to find the difference between the two numbers, halve the difference, then add it to the lower number.
- Give each child or pair of children a sub-set of six cards from PCM 21. (The cards in a sub-set are all labelled A, B, C or D, and each sub-set comprises a complete self-checking loop or chain.) Demonstrate the different question/answer sections on the cards. Children arrange the cards in question/answer order and make a complete chain, with the question on the last card being answered by the answer on the first card. Children work together to make a chain using all four sub-sets of cards.
- When all of the group are ready, shuffle the 24 cards together and deal them out to children. One child plays a card, then play passes to their right. If the next player has a card that answers the question on the first card (regardless of A, B, C or D notation), they play it; if they don't, they 'pass' and play continues to move to the right. Play continues until one player has no cards left and is the winner. Note: For best results, the first card to be played should display the answer 100 (there are four of these).

Further extension
In pairs, children can try to make their own set of six ordering numbers linking cards, like the cards on the PCM.

If you have time
Play the game again, faster this time. If appropriate, allow a 'play when you can go' rule, instead of taking turns.

Be aware

- Check whether children are struggling with finding the number exactly half-way between a pair of numbers early on when they are working on the individual loops of six cards. If so, pair up children and spend longer on this aspect before the game.

Outcomes

- I can order sets of 3-digit numbers and pick out the largest and smallest number.
- I can add and subtract 2- and 3-digit numbers in my head.
- I can find small differences between numbers by counting on.

Supporting resources

Ordering games can be found at:
- http://www.tldsb.on.ca/Schools/GrandviewPS/Room_108/sequence/sequence.htm
- http://www.ictgames.com/caterpillar_slider.html

Summary

Y3 ○ A2.3

Timelines

Pairs or groups working independently

Year 3 Challenge Textbook page 30

Strips of A3 paper; metre rulers; reference books; internet (optional)

Abacus Evolve objectives

- Order numbers up to at least 1000
- Say a number lying between two 3-digit numbers
- Count on in 10s, 100s or 50s from zero
- Use units of time and know the relationship between them: years, months, weeks, days, hours
- Use a ruler to draw and measure lines to the nearest half centimetre

Framework objectives

- Read, write and order whole numbers to at least 1000 and position them on a number line; count on from and back to zero in single-digit steps or multiples of 10
- Read the time on a 12-hour digital clock and to the nearest 5 minutes on an analogue clock; calculate time intervals and find start or end times for a given time interval
- *Read, to the nearest division and half-division, scales that are numbered or partially numbered; use the information to measure and draw to a suitable degree of accuracy*
- Sustain conversation, explaining or giving reasons for their views or choices

Teacher notes

Preparation
Cut sheets of A3 paper into long paper strips that children can join to make timelines.

Activity
Children work from Textbook page 30. They learn about timelines, and start by making a timeline showing the important events in their lifetime.
Children then make a timeline of the last 100 years. They join paper strips together and then rule, mark and date the timeline, writing the decades from 1910 to 2010. They choose some important events from the Textbook page to write on their timeline, and research others, using reference books and the internet, if available. Encourage them to estimate the positions of events which occur between the multiples of 10 years.

Further extension
Children make a timeline for the last 1000 years, using a similar approach as the 100-year timeline, but making each 10 cm interval represent 100 years. Use the websites below to search for important events and dates.

If you have time
Children make a timeline of significant events in their own life. If they like they can continue it into the future and imagine what might happen to them and when.

Be aware

- Children may have trouble placing years such as 1914 on the timeline, because there is no marked division for this. Reassure them that their placement doesn't have to be exact, and that they should place the year as close as possible to where they think it should go.

Outcomes

- I can draw a timeline that counts up in 10s.
- I can work out where a number should go on a scale that does not have every division marked.

Supporting resources

Sources of dates:
- http://www.johnowensmith.co.uk/histdate/
- http://www.infoplease.com/ipa/A0781458.html

A2: rounding to the nearest 10; ordering numbers to 1000; counting on in 10s, 100s or 50s; odd and even numbers

Summary

Y3 ◯ A2.4	**Counting sequences**	
	Individuals or pairs working independently	
	Year 3 Challenge Textbook page 31	
	Calculators	

Abacus Evolve objectives

- Count on and back in 100s from any number
- Count on in 10s, 100s or 50s from zero
- Say the number that is 1, 10 or 100 more or less than any 2- or 3-digit number
- Count on in 5s to 100, and in 50s to 1000
- Add and subtract a multiple of 10 to and from a 3-digit number, crossing 100

Framework objectives

- Read, write and order whole numbers to at least 1000 and position them on a number line; count on from and back to zero in single-digit steps or multiples of 10
- *Add or subtract mentally combinations of 1- and 2-digit numbers*
- Follow up others' points and show whether they agree or disagree in a whole-class discussion

Teacher notes

Getting started
Demonstrate how to use a calculator to generate sequences by adding or subtracting numbers repeatedly to or from a given number.

Activity
Children work from Textbook page 31. First they work in pairs, counting on or back in steps of 5, 10, 50, 100, 500 or 1000 from given numbers. One child writes the sequence while the other uses a calculator to generate the sequence and checks that the first child is correct.
Children are then given pairs of start and end numbers, and they are asked to decide whether to count on or back in steps of 5, 10, 50, 100, 500 or 1000 to get from one to the other. They record two of these sequences and record the numbers in the sequence and the number of steps needed.
For the first two sequences the start number is 0. In working out that there are, for example, seven steps of 50 to get from 0 to 350, children will realise that there are seven 50s in 350. If appropriate, make the link to 7 × 50 = 350.

Extra help
Children can start by practising with patterns such as:
start at 20, count on in 5s to 60
Start at 40, count on in 15s to 100.

Further extension
Children can explore other patterns with steps of 25, 175, and 125. They can then move on to look at patterns with steps that are not a multiple of 5.

If you have time
Show children 1 ÷ 2 on a calculator. *This shows that $\frac{1}{2}$ is 0·5 as a decimal*. Children can start to work at patterns counting on and back in halves, using 0·5.
Start at 20, count on in halves to 25
Start at 25, count back in halves to 20

Be aware

- A common misconception is to misunderstand place value in large numbers, e.g. thinking that 5045 − 500 = 45. With a little support, however, children should overcome this difficulty.

Outcomes

- I can count on and back in 10s, 100s and 1000s from any number.
- I can use a calculator to make sure my partner is adding and subtracting correctly.

Challenge Plan: Year 3

A2: rounding to the nearest 10; ordering numbers to 1000; counting on in 10s, 100s or 50s; odd and even numbers

Summary

Y3 ⬡ A2.5

Counting on and back

A small group working with an adult

Year 3 Challenge PCM 22

Abacus Evolve objectives

- **Y4** Add or subtract 1, 10, 100 or 1000 to or from any integer
- **Y4** Count on and back in 1s, 10s, 100s or 1000s from any whole number up to 100 000

Framework objectives

- **Y4** Partition, round and order 4-digit whole numbers; use positive and negative numbers in context and position them on a number line; state inequalities using the symbols < and >, e.g. $-3 > -5$, $-1 < +1$
- **Y4** Solve one- and two-step problems involving numbers, money or measures, including time; choose and carry out appropriate calculations, using calculator methods where appropriate
- **Y4** Respond appropriately to others in the light of alternative viewpoints

Teacher notes

Preparation
Photocopy PCM 22 onto thin card. Cut out the 20 number cards and the 20 money cards.

Activity
- Give children the 20 numbers cards from the top section of PCM 22. Children find pairs of numbers in which one number can be made into the other number in three steps, choosing from any of ± 5, ± 10, ± 50, ± 100 and ± 500 (there is no limit on the number of times a step can be used). For example, 39 can be made into 134 by: $39 + 5 - 10 + 100 = 134$.
- Encourage children to explore different ways to link the same pair. For example, $39 - 10 + 100 + 5 = 134$, or $134 + 10 - 5 - 100 = 39$. Also encourage them to look for patterns in units digits when looking for pairs.
- Once numbers are paired up, two numbers will be left (77 and 737). *How can you make 77 into 737 by adding or subtracting 5, 10, 50, 100 or 500?* ($77 + 100 + 500 + 50 + 10 = 737$)
- Divide the 20 money cards from the bottom section of PCM 22 into the four sub-sets (W, X, Y and Z). Give each child or pair one sub-set. They put them in order, then work out how to get from one amount to the next in each set, using combinations of $\pm 5p$, $\pm 10p$, $\pm 50p$, $\pm £1$, $\pm £5$ and $\pm £10$, in the fewest number of steps. They record the total number of steps needed to get from the first to the last in each set. (In each set, two or three steps are needed between each amount, with a total of 10 steps per set.)

Extra help
For the first part of the activity, you could tell children some or all of the pairs: 39 and 134; 56 and 201; 72 and 422; 37 and 487; 61 and 216; 106 and 711; 317 and 272; 109 and 699; 62 and 522.

Further extension
Challenge children to start at 5000 and make three different moves from ± 10, ± 50, ± 100, ± 500, ± 1000. Each number can only be used once, for example 10 can be used once, either to add or subtract. Children explore how many different end numbers can be reached using these rules.

If you have time
Children can work in pairs to make their own set of six counting on and back linking cards, like the cards on the PCM.

Be aware

- Children may not be familiar with calculations such as £15·99 + 10p. Help them to recognise that £15·99 + 10p is only 1p away from £16 + 10p.

Outcomes

- I can get from one number to another using a combination of steps, such as +5, +10, −100.
- I can add and subtract 5, 10, 100 and 1000 to and from any number or amount of money.

Summary

Y3 A2.6

Olympic rings

Pairs working independently

Year 3 Challenge Textbook page 32

Year 3 Challenge PCM 23

Abacus Evolve objectives	Framework objectives
• Recognise odd and even numbers up to at least 50 • Add and subtract two 2-digit numbers, beginning to cross a multiple of 10 • Add and subtract a 2-digit number to and from a 3-digit number	• Identify patterns and relationships involving numbers or shapes and use these to solve problems • *Add or subtract mentally combinations of 1- and 2-digit numbers* • Follow a line of enquiry by deciding what information is important; make and use lists, tables and graphs to organise and interpret the information • Describe and explain methods, choices and solutions to puzzles and problems, orally and in writing, using pictures and diagrams • Sustain conversation, explaining or giving reasons for their views or choices

Teacher notes

Preparing
Photocopy PCM 23, one copy per pair.

Activity
Children work from Textbook page 32. They are shown a set of five intersecting rings, with a number written in each ring and overlapping section. They should notice that the numbers within each ring add up to the same total: 125.
Children are given sets of numbers to write in intersecting rings so that the numbers within each ring add to the same total. They are encouraged to talk about patterns that they notice.
Children are then given an incomplete set of numbers and asked to work out the missing number, and a set of numbers which contains a superfluous number which they must identify.
Having established patterns in the arrangements of the numbers, children then explore other sets of nine numbers that add to the same totals.

Extra help
Look at the completed pattern on the Textbook page. *Where is the smallest number? The next smallest number?* Children can use what they notice in the completed pattern to help them complete other patterns.

Information
When looking for patterns, children might notice a similarity between their answers to question 3 and question 6. The values in question 6 have been multiplied by 10. Children should also notice that the smallest number and the largest number are always in the same place in the pattern. The numbers in between are also always in the same place, from smallest to largest.

Be aware	Outcomes
• Children may need some support and encouragement to work systematically and logically.	• I can work out the answer to puzzles by trying different solutions and seeing if they work. • I can add 2- and 3-digit numbers, choosing the method I find easiest.

Supporting resources

A 4 × 4 magic square puzzle, to practise mental addition and thinking strategies:
• http://www.puzzlepixies.com/impossible/impossible/magic-square-4x4.htm

Challenge Plan: Year 3

Summary

Y3 B2.1

Using multiples to add and subtract

Individuals, pairs or groups working independently

Year 3 Challenge Textbook page 33

Abacus Evolve objectives

- Rehearse pairs of multiples of 10 that total 100
- Derive all pairs of multiples of 5 that total 100
- Round numbers less than 100 to the nearest 10
- Add and subtract a multiple of 10 to and from a 2-digit number, crossing 100 when adding
- Add and subtract two 2-digit numbers, beginning to cross a multiple of 10
- Add and subtract 19 and 29 to and from a 2- or 3-digit number

Framework objectives

- *Derive and recall all addition and subtraction facts for each number to 20, sums and differences of multiples of 10 and number pairs that total 100*
- *Add or subtract mentally combinations of 1-digit and 2-digit numbers*
- Solve one- and two-step problems involving numbers, money or measures, including time, choosing and carrying out appropriate calculations

Teacher notes

Getting started
Work through some simple additions and subtractions with 2-digit multiples of 5 and 10, e.g. 35 + 25, 60 − 15.

Activity
Children work from Textbook page 33. They complete some additions and subtractions with 2-digit multiples of 5 and 10, and make up some of their own.
Children then look at a number line modelling a more complex subtraction. They are shown how to find an approximate answer using multiples of 5 and 10 and then make a mental adjustment, counting on or back to the correct answer.
Children use this method to work out the given additions and subtractions, then make up their own examples.

Extra help
Practise with a short mental subtraction exercise. Start with multiples of 5 and 10, e.g. 100 2 50. Then adjust one or other of the numbers by 1 or 2 each way, e.g. 100 − 49 (51), 100 − 52 (48), 99 − 50 (51)

Further extension
Extend numbers beyond 200, up to 500. Ask children to make up problems with these larger numbers and exchange them with a partner.

Be aware

- Children may make errors when adjusting their answer at the end of the calculation. They may find a number line helpful.

Outcomes

- I can add and subtract numbers ending in 5 or 0 in my head.
- I can round 2-digit numbers to the nearest 5 or 10.
- I can use rounding to help me work out more difficult calculations in my head.

Challenge Plan: Year 3

B2: pairs of multiples of 100 that total 1000; using pairs to 100 to make the next multiple of 100; prisms; 3D shapes

Summary

Y3 ⭐ **B2.2**

Adding and subtracting

Individuals, pairs or groups working independently

Year 3 Challenge Textbook page 34

Digit cards

Abacus Evolve objectives

- **Y4** Derive quickly pairs of numbers that total 100
- **Y4** Derive quickly pairs of multiples of 5 that total 100
- **Y4** Find what to add to a 2- or 3-digit number to make 100 or the next multiple of 100
- **Y4** Find what to add to a 4-digit multiple of 100 to make the next multiple of 1000
- **Y4** Add and subtract 2- and 3-digit multiples of 10
- **Y4** Add and subtract two multiples of 100, crossing 1000
- **Y4** Recognise decimal notation in the context of money

Framework objectives

- **Y4** Use knowledge of addition and subtraction facts and place value to derive sums and differences of pairs of multiples of 10, 100 or 1000
- **Y4** Use decimal notation for tenths and hundredths and partition decimals; relate the notation to money and measurement; position 1- and 2-place decimals on a number line
- **Y4** Solve one-step and two-step problems involving numbers, money or measures, including time; choose and carry out appropriate calculations, using calculator methods where appropriate

---

Teacher notes

Getting started

Work through some simple additions, adding 3-digit multiples of 10 or 100 to make a 3- or 4-digit multiple of 100 or 1000, e.g. 300 + 400 = 700, 140 + 360 = 500. Ask children to make up some of their own.

Activity

Children work from Textbook page 34. They solve missing-number additions involving multiples of 10 and 100.
They then find all the pairs of decade numbers (multiples of 10) that total 200.
Children decide what coin/note they would use to pay for given items, and work out how much change they would get.
Children then look at subtractions that each have the same answer and explore fixed differences.

Extra help

Chldren can start by exploring pairs of numbers that make 20. Help them to make the link between these and pairs that total 200, e.g. 13 + 7 = 20, 130 + 70 = 200

Further extension

Chlidren use all ten digit cards and try to make an addition and a subtraction that have the same answer, e.g. 58 + 6 and 73 − 9. This example uses six of the digit cards. Can children find other examples that use six cards? Seven cards? All ten cards?

Be aware

- When calculating sums of money children should be expected to count mentally, perhaps with jottings. Written methods would be too cumbersome for these problems.

Outcomes

- I can work backwards to work out the question if I know the answer.
- I can work out what you need to add to a number to make it up to the next 100 or 1000.
- I can add and subtract amounts of money by counting.

Supporting resources

Children can play Game 1 and Game 2, which both involve giving change:
- http://www.bbc.co.uk/skillswise/numbers/measuring/money/game.shtml

Challenge Plan: Year 3

B2: pairs of multiples of 100 that total 1000; using pairs to 100 to make the next multiple of 100; prisms; 3D shapes

Summary

Y3 ⭐ **B2.3**

Complements linking cards

 A small group working with an adult

📓 Year 3 Challenge PCM 24

✍️ Thin card; calculators (optional)

Abacus Evolve objectives

- Rehearse pairs of multiples of 10 that total 100
- Know by heart pairs of multiples of 100 that total 1000
- Derive all pairs of multiples of 5 that total 100
- Derive all number pairs that total 100
- Use pairs that total 100 to make the next multiple of 100
- Understand and use £.p notation

Framework objectives

- *Derive and recall all addition and subtraction facts for each number to 20, sums and differences of multiples of 10 and number pairs that total 100*
- Solve one-step and two-step problems involving numbers, money or measures, including time, choosing and carrying out appropriate calculations
- Actively include and respond to all members of the group

Teacher notes

Preparation
Photocopy PCM 24 onto thin A4 card and cut out the cards.

Activity
- Ask children to find complements of:
  - 2-digit numbers to 100, e.g. *What would you add to 13 to make 1000?*
  - 3-digit numbers to 1000, e.g. *What would you add to 710 to make 1000?*
  - amounts of money to £10, e.g. *What would you add to £5·40 to make £10?*
- Give each child or pair a sub-set of six cards from PCM 24. (The cards in a sub-set are all labelled A, B, C or D, and each sub-set comprises a complete self-checking loop or chain.) Ask them to put their cards in order so that each question appears before its answer. This involves finding complements to 100, 1000 and £10.
- Children work as a group to make a chain using all four sub-sets of cards.
- When all of the group are ready, shuffle the pack of 24 cards and deal them out to the children. One child plays a card, then play passes to their left. If the next player has a card that answers the question on the first card (regardless of A, B, C or D notation), they play it; if they don't, they 'pass' and play continues to move to the left. Play continues until one player has no cards left and is the winner. For best results, the first card to be played should display the answer 24 (there are four of these in the pack).

If you have time
Play the game again so that children can play it faster. If appropriate, allow a 'play when you can go' rule, instead of taking turns.

Be aware

- A number line may be helpful for children who need support with finding complements to 100 or 1000.

Outcomes

- I can quickly work out what you need to add to a number to make 100 or 1000.
- I know by heart some pairs of numbers that total 100 and 1000.

Supporting resources

Children can practise number bonds at:
- http://www.amblesideprimary.com/ambleweb/mentalmaths/numberbond.html

B2: pairs of multiples of 100 that total 1000; using pairs to 100 to make the next multiple of 100; prisms; 3D shapes

Summary

Y3 ○ B2.4	**Making 3D stars**
	A small group working with an adult
	Year 3 Challenge Textbook page 35
	Regular polygons; regular prisms with all edge lengths equal

Abacus Evolve objectives

- Introduce, classify and describe prisms
- Relate prisms to pictures of them
- Classify and describe common 3D shapes by properties: number of faces, edges, vertices; types of face
- Identify and sketch lines of symmetry in simple shapes

Framework objectives

- Relate 2D shapes and 3D solids to drawings of them; describe, visualise, classify, draw and make the shapes
- Follow a line of enquiry by deciding what information is important; make and use lists, tables and graphs to organise and interpret the information
- Identify patterns and relationships involving numbers or shapes, and use these to solve problems
- Develop and use specific vocabulary in different contexts

Teacher notes

Activity

- Show children a set of regular polygons. Discuss the lines of symmetry of each one.
- Children work from Textbook page 35. Work on questions 1 and 2 together. Confirm that polygons with an even number of sides have lines of symmetry between opposite vertices and between opposite mid-points, while polygons with an odd number of sides have lines of symmetry from each vertex to the opposite mid-point. (Number of sides = number of vertices = number of lines of symmetry.)
- Show children a set of prisms with all edge lengths equal. Discuss their properties. (Each has a regular polygon 'top and bottom'.)
- Explain what a plane of symmetry is. Ask children to discuss the planes of symmetry of each prism. (Each prism has a plane of symmetry half-way along its length. The other planes of symmetry match the lines of symmetry of the regular polygon.)
- Children then explore the effects of adding triangular-based pyramids and square-based pyramids onto the faces of a triangular prism, to make a star-shaped polyhedron. They explore what happens when the same is done to a regular hexagonal prism, and record in a table how the numbers of vertices and faces change as the pyramids are added.
- Encourage children to recognise patterns in the tables and come to some general conclusions about them. (The number of vertices of the star polyhedron is the sum of the vertices and faces of the original prism. Every star polyhedron has a number of faces that is a multiple of 3.) They use these conclusions to predict the number of vertices and faces on a star polyhedron made from a regular pentagonal prism.

Be aware

- Children may have some difficulties in recording their data systematically. Encourage them to use the table format to help them spot patterns.
- Make sure children are confident in using new terminology such as *polyhedra* and *planes of symmetry*.

Outcomes

- I can find lines of symmetry on 2D shapes.
- I can find planes of symmetry on 3D shapes.
- I can count faces, vertices and edges of 3D shapes.
- I can make a table and use it to find patterns.

Supporting resources

A symmetry sorting activity can be found at:
- http://www.crickweb.co.uk/assets/resources/flash.php?&file=Symm

Challenge Plan: Year 3

B2: pairs of multiples of 100 that total 1000; using pairs to 100 to make the next multiple of 100; prisms; 3D shapes

Summary

Y3 ⬡ **B2.5**

The Soma cube

Individuals, pairs or groups working independently

Year 3 Challenge Textbook page 36

 Linking cubes; triangle dot paper (optional); digital cameras (optional); internet (optional)

◁|∘∘∘|▷ Abacus Evolve objectives

- Classify and describe common 3D shapes by properties: number of faces, edges, vertices, types of face
- Relate prisms to pictures of them
- Identify and sketch lines of symmetry in simple shapes

Framework objectives

- Relate 2D shapes and 3D solids to drawings of them; describe, visualise, classify, draw and make the shapes
- *Draw and complete shapes with reflective symmetry and draw the reflection of a shape in a mirror line along one side*
- Describe and explain methods, choices and solutions to puzzles and problems, orally and in writing, using pictures and diagrams

Teacher notes

Getting started
Demonstrate linking three or four cubes to make 3D shapes (not including cuboids). Ask children to make a few of their own.

Activity
Children work from Textbook page 36. They learn about Piet Hein's Soma cube, and try to make the seven shapes from which the Soma cube is made. Children try to make the Soma cube from their seven shapes.
They make symmetrical shapes using their seven shapes, and then make three famous symmetrical 3D arrangements. Children could photograph their shapes as they make them, or draw their shapes on triangle dot paper.

Further extension
Children can use the internet to research the Steinhaus cube, designed by Hugo Steinhaus. It is similar to the Soma cube, but has some interesting differences. What differences can children find?

Information
The Soma cube is a 3 by 3 by 3 cube made from seven shapes. Each shape is made from three or four smaller cubes, and none of them is a cuboid. There are 240 distinct solutions of the basic Soma cube puzzle, excluding rotations and reflections of these. Very many puzzle shapes can be made from the seven pieces, although relatively few are symmetrical.

Be aware

- Children sometimes have difficulty visualising what is there but cannot be seen in 3D pictures of shapes. Actually making the shapes such as the castle and the pyramid should help with this.

Outcomes

- I can find all the different ways to join three and four cubes together.
- I can work out how to join these together to make a 3 by 3 by 3 cube.
- I can make other symmetrical shapes using the shapes I have made.

Supporting resources

Information about the Soma cube can be found here:
- http://www.bbc.co.uk/dna/h2g2/A1064936

Information about the Steinhaus cube can be found here:
- www.johnrausch.com/PuzzlingWorld.chap03a.htm

Challenge Plan: Year 3

B2: pairs of multiples of 100 that total 1000; using pairs to 100 to make the next multiple of 100; prisms; 3D shapes

Summary

 Y3 ☆ B2.6   **Prisms and anti-prisms**

 Individuals, pairs or groups working independently

Year 3 Challenge Textbook page 37

Year 3 Challenge PCM 25

 Squared paper; regular shapes (optional); sticky tape (optional)

Abacus Evolve objectives

- **Y4** Begin to use the terms 'polyhedron' and 'tetrahedron'
- **Y4** Describe and visualise 3D shapes
- **Y4** Rehearse the names of common 3D shapes
- **Y4** Visualise 3D shapes from 2D drawings and identify simple nets of solid shapes
- **Y4** Make and investigate a general statement about familiar numbers or shapes by finding examples that satisfy it (shape)

Framework objectives

- **Y4** Visualise 3D objects from 2D drawings and make nets of common solids
- **Y4** Identify and use patterns, relationships and properties of numbers or shapes; investigate a statement involving numbers and test it with examples
- **Y4** Suggest a line of enquiry and the strategy needed to follow it; collect, organise and interpret selected information to find answers

Teacher notes

Preparation
Photocopy PCM 25, one copy per child, pair or group. If possible, enlarge it to make the nets easier for children to work with.

Activity
Children work from Textbook page 37. They copy the nets of a cuboid and a triangular prism onto squared paper and construct the 3D shapes.
They then look at the nets on PCM 25, identify if they are real polyhedron nets and amend them if they are not. They construct the polyhedra from the nets and name them.
Children then compare prisms and anti-prisms and record their results in the tables on the PCM. Children should notice that prisms and anti-prisms with the same base have different numbers of edges and faces but the same number of vertices, and they share all but one plane of symmetry.

Extra help
Children may find it helpful to make models of the prisms and anti-prisms in the tables using squares, equilateral triangles and regular polygons.

Information
An anti-prism is a polyhedron formed from two regular shapes, twisted 45° relative to each other, with a set of triangles joining the two regular shapes.

Be aware

- Identifying nets and their corresponding shapes is not an easy concept. Making supposed nets into shapes will help children develop their understanding.
- Make sure children are confident in using new terminology such as *polyhedra* and *planes of symmetry*.

Outcomes

- I can draw nets of common 3D shapes and then test to see if I was right by constructing them.
- I can identify nets for different 3D solids.
- I can describe and name different 3D shapes.
- I can make a table and use it to find patterns.

Supporting resources

Demonstrations of how nets fold to make polyhedra can be found at:
- http://www.fi.uu.nl/toepassingen/00297/toepassing_wisweb.en.html
- http://www.cs.mcgill.ca/~sqrt/unfold/unfolding.html

Challenge Plan: Year 3

C2: capacities in litres and millilitres; units of time (days, hours, minutes, seconds); frequency tables; bar charts

Summary

Y3 C2.1

Calibrating capacities

Pairs or groups working independently

Year 3 Challenge Textbook page 38

2 litre clear plastic bottles; 100 ml bottles; 50 ml bottles; strips of sticky paper; dry lentils; A4 paper; a range of empty containers (uncalibrated)

Abacus Evolve objectives

- Measure and compare capacities using standard units: litres, millilitres
- Know the relationship between litres and millilitres
- Read a capacity scale to the nearest labelled and unlabelled division

Framework objectives

- Know the relationships between kilometres and metres, metres and centimetres, kilograms and grams, litres and millilitres; choose and use appropriate units to estimate, measure and record measurements
- *Read, to the nearest division and half-division, scales that are numbered or partially numbered; use the information to measure and draw to a suitable degree of accuracy*
- Solve one- and two-step problems involving numbers, money or measures, including time, choosing and carrying out appropriate calculations

Teacher notes

Preparation
Make sure you have one of each size of bottle and 2 litres of lentils per pair or group.

Getting started
Demonstrate making a cone from A4 paper and cutting the tip off to make a funnel.

Activity
Children work from Textbook page 38. They investigate producing a calibrated bottle using 100 ml and 50 ml measures of lentils. They use their calibrated bottle to measure, by lentil transfer, other unmarked containers.
As the purpose of the exercise is to deepen understanding of capacity, children's calibrated bottles need not be highly accurate.

Further extension
A depth gauge is used to measure the depth inside a container.
Children work in pairs to try and design a simple depth gauge. Remind them that they are now measuring depth, not capacity so they should use suitable units (if necessary, suggest cm or mm.)

If you have time
Children can develop their estimation skills by playing the estimating game from Activity C1.1, but basing it on capacity rather than length. They use their calibrated bottle to check the answers.

Be aware

- Children working with scale may assume that each interval always represents one unit. Encourage children to think about why this might not always be the case and to think about sensible intervals for their bottles.

Outcomes

- I can mark known amounts to create a scale on a bottle.
- I know the relationship between millilitres and litres.
- I can read measures off my scale that are not an exact amount, by estimating between two intervals.

Supporting resources

Children can practise using scales at:
- http://www.channel4learning.net/sites/puzzlemaths/pinpoint_game.shtml

Challenge Plan: Year 3

C2: capacities in litres and millilitres; units of time (days, hours, minutes, seconds); frequency tables; bar charts

---

Summary

Y3 **C2.2**

Calculating capacities

A small group working with an adult

Year 3 Challenge Textbook page 39

Abacus Evolve objectives

- **Y4** Use, read and write standard metric units of capacity: l, ml
- **Y4** Rehearse the relationship between litres and millilitres
- **Y4** Know the equivalent of $\frac{1}{2}$, $\frac{1}{4}$, $\frac{3}{4}$, $\frac{1}{10}$ of 1 litre in ml
- **Y4** Record estimates and readings from capacity scales

Framework objectives

- **Y4** Choose and use standard metric units and their abbreviations when estimating, measuring and recording length, weight and capacity; know the meaning of 'kilo', 'centi' and 'milli' and, where appropriate, use decimal notation to record measurements, e.g. 1·3 m or 0·6 kg
- **Y4** Interpret intervals and divisions on partially numbered scales and record readings accurately, where appropriate to the nearest tenth of a unit
- **Y4** Solve one-step and two-step problems involving numbers, money or measures, including time; choose and carry out appropriate calculations, using calculator methods where appropriate

---

Teacher notes

Activity
- Ask children to convert a few millilitre amounts into litres, and vice versa. For example: *How many litres is 3000 millilitres? How many millilitres is 1·75 litres?*
- Children work from Textbook page 39. They answer conversion questions involving litres and millilitres, true/false capacity questions and questions about the capacities of given containers.
- As a group, make up and solve some word problems involving millilitres and litres, using the containers on the Textbook page. For example: *How much would be left in the 1·5 litre container after it has been used to fill the 700 ml container? What combination of containers 'equal' 1 litre?*

Extra help
Provide children with a simple table to help with converting between millilitres and litres. Fill in the first line with 1000 millilitres and 1 litre. Help children to fill in other values such as 500 millilitres and $\frac{1}{2}$ litre, 2000 millilitres and 2 litres.

Further extension
How many 50 ml bottles can be filled from containers with these capacities? 1 litre, 1.5 litres, 2 litres, 5 litres, 10 litres. How many 75 ml bottles? How many 25 ml bottles?

Be aware

- Children may have difficulty converting between millilitres and litres. Remind them that there are 1000 millilitres in a litre.

Outcomes

- I know what some simple fractions of 1 litre are in millilitres.
- I can read scales and work out the capacity of different containers.
- I can use dividing, counting up in 10s, or repeated addition to work out how many times a number goes into a larger number.

Supporting resources

This game gives children practice in reading capacities
- http://www.bgfl.org/bgfl/custom/resources_ftp/client_ftp/ks2/maths/measures/index.htm

Challenge Plan: Year 3

C2: capacities in litres and millilitres; units of time (days, hours, minutes, seconds); frequency tables; bar charts

Summary

Y3 ⬡ C2.3

Record times

Individuals, pairs or groups working independently

Year 3 Challenge Textbook page 40

Year 3 Challenge PCM 26

Calculators; internet (optional)

Abacus Evolve objectives

- Use units of time and know the relationship between them: days, hours, minutes, seconds
- Use units of time and know the relationship between them: years, months, weeks, days, hours
- Solve problems involving time: say the number of minutes earlier or later than a given 5-minute time
- Round numbers less than 100 to the nearest 10
- Add and subtract two 2-digit numbers, beginning to cross a multiple of 10
- Find a difference between two 2- or 3-digit numbers by counting on

Framework objectives

- Read the time on a 12-hour digital clock and to the nearest 5 minutes on an analogue clock; calculate time intervals and find start or end times for a given time interval
- Round 2- or 3-digit numbers to the nearest 10 or 100 and give estimates for their sums and differences
- *Add or subtract mentally combinations of 1-digit and 2-digit numbers*
- Solve one-step and two-step problems involving numbers, money or measures, including time, choosing and carrying out appropriate calculations

Teacher notes

Preparation
Photocopy PCM 26, one copy per child, pair or group.

Getting started
Show children the sporting results on PCM 26. Discuss why there might be differences between each pair of results.

Activity
Children work from Textbook page 40. They use the data on the PCM to answer questions about differences between times, using minutes, seconds and days.

Further extension
Look at the current world record for 100 metres. Double it to make a time for 200 metres. Find out the actual world record for 200 metres. *How much slower is it than the doubled time for 100 metres?* Do the same for the 200 metres and 400 metres records, then the 400 metres and the 800 metres records. Discuss why the records are not just doubles of the half distances. (Children should consider runners tiring and slowing down the further they run.)

If you have time
Children can use data from reference books and the internet to pose similar questions for each other.

Be aware

- Some children forget, when calculating, that there are 60 minutes in one hour rather than 100, because they are so used to decimal systems.

Outcomes

- I know the relationship between minutes, seconds, hours and days.
- I can change one unit of time to another.

Supporting resources

Games involving time can be found at:
- http://www.bgfl.org/bgfl/custom/resources_ftp/client_ftp/ks2/maths/timetables/index.htm
- http://www.bbc.co.uk/skillswise/numbers/measuring/time/calculatingtime/game.shtml

Summary

Y3 C2.4

Frequency tables

A small group working with an adult

Year 3 Challenge PCM 27

Internet (optional)

Abacus Evolve objectives

- **Y4** Represent data in frequency tables
- **Y4** Interpret tally charts and frequency tables
- **Y4** Construct and interpret bar graphs with intervals labelled in 2s, 5s, 10s or 20s

Framework objectives

- **Y4** *Answer a question by identifying what data to collect; organise, present, analyse and interpret the data in tables, diagrams, tally charts, pictograms and bar charts, using ICT where appropriate*
- **Y4** *Suggest a line of enquiry and the strategy needed to follow it; collect, organise and interpret selected information to find answers*
- **Y4** *Use and reflect on some ground rules for dialogue (e.g. making structured, extended contributions, speaking audibly, making meaning explicit and listening actively)*

Teacher notes

Preparation
Photocopy PCM 27, one copy per child.

Activity
- Look together at the table on PCM 27. It presents information from birdwatchers about the 36 species of birds spotted and recorded in a 1 km square grid reference. *Which birds were seen the most? The least?*
- Ask questions that require children to organise and tabulate the data. For example:
  - *How many birdwatchers do you think took part in the survey?* (At least 20)
  - *How many species were recorded by 1–5 birdwatchers? 6–10? 11–15? 16–20?* (Encourage children to construct a simple table dividing the data into four groups, and from this draw a simple bar chart.)
  - *How would the bar chart have looked different if the data was divided into 10 groups (1–2, 3–4, etc)?*
  - *What does the data tell us about the bird populations? Do any species have very low population levels?*

If you have time
Ask children to explore the data for your school's grid reference using the weblink below.

Be aware

- Encourage children to think carefully about how the data is grouped so that they do not include any values twice.

Outcomes

- I can suggest ways to organise a set of data.
- I can sort data into groups and record this in a table.
- I can draw a bar graph using data from a table.
- I can describe what a bar graph shows.

Supporting resources

Find out about the Big School Birdwatch and Wildsquare at:
- http://www.rspb.org.uk/schoolswatch/index.asp
- http://www.rspb.org.uk/wildsquare/index.asp

Children can use this tool to create their own bar graph:
- http://www.amblesideprimary.com/ambleweb/mentalmaths/grapher.html

Summary

Y3 ⭐ **C2.5**	**Box-and-whisker plots**
	Individuals, pairs or groups working independently
	Year 3 Challenge Textbook page 41
	Year 3 Challenge PCM 28
	Rulers; pencils

Abacus Evolve objectives

- Solve a given problem by organising and interpreting numerical data in simple lists, tally charts and frequency tables
- Organise and interpret numerical data in frequency tables
- Organise and interpret numerical data in bar charts
- Order numbers up to at least 1000
- Find a difference between two 2- or 3-digit numbers by counting on
- Add and subtract two 2-digit numbers, beginning to cross a multiple of 10

Framework objectives

- Answer a question by collecting, organising and interpreting data; use tally charts, frequency tables, pictograms and bar charts to represent results and illustrate observations; use ICT to create a simple bar chart
- Read, write and order whole numbers to at least 1000 and position them on a number line; count on from and back to zero in single-digit steps or multiples of 10
- *Add or subtract mentally combinations of 1-digit and 2-digit numbers*

Teacher notes

Preparation
Photocopy PCM 28, one copy per child, pair or group.

Getting started
Look together at the data on PCM 28. Briefly discuss the different times of the 23 runners.

Activity
Children work from Textbook page 41. They find the fastest and slowest times, and the range.
Children then learn about box-and-whisker plots and follow instructions to construct their own. With a scale of one square to 10 seconds, children should be able to work to within $+/-1$ second of accuracy.
Children should appreciate that this way of plotting data is relatively simple and yet gives a good picture of the data.

Extra help
Introduce children to the key ideas in the exercise, with a few examples. E.g. the number of questions answered in one minute by seven children: 9, 10, 12, 13, 14, 16, 18. *What is the range?* $18 - 9 = 9$. *What is the median?* The median (the middle number) is 13. *Now find the middle number of the values either side of the median.* 10 and 16. *10 is called the lower quartile and 16 is called the upper quartile.* Take the lower quartile from the upper quartile to find the interquartile range. $16 - 10 = 6$. Ask children to draw a box-and-whisker plot to show this.

Be aware

- Children may have difficulty finding the middle value of a set of data. They may mind it helpful to cross off one value from each end of an ordered list in turn.

Outcomes

- I can find the range of a set of data by subtracting the smallest value from the largest.
- I can pick out the smallest, the largest and the middle number from a set of data.
- I can draw a box-and-whisker plot from a set of data.
- I can identify facts about a set of data from a box-and-whisker plot.

Supporting resources

Box-and-whisker plots can be created online at:
- http://www.mrnussbaum.com/graph/bw.htm

Challenge Plan: Year 3

C2: capacities in litres and millilitres; units of time (days, hours, minutes, seconds); frequency tables; bar charts

Summary

Y3 ☆ C2.6

Star names and real names

Individuals, pairs or groups working independently

Year 3 Challenge Textbook page 42

Year 3 Challenge PCM 29

Internet (optional)

Abacus Evolve objectives	Framework objectives
• Solve a given problem by organising and interpreting numerical data in simple lists, tally charts and frequency tables • Organise and interpret numerical data in frequency tables • Organise and interpret numerical data in bar charts	• Answer a question by collecting, organising and interpreting data; use tally charts, frequency tables, pictograms and bar charts to represent results and illustrate observations; use ICT to create a simple bar chart • Follow a line of enquiry by deciding what information is important; make and use lists, tables and graphs to organise and interpret the information • Explain a process or present information, ensuring items are clearly sequenced, relevant details are included and accounts ended effectively

Teacher notes

Preparation
Photocopy PCM 29, one copy per child.

Activity
Children work from Textbook page 42. They look at the star names and real names of 28 celebrities on PCM 29 and make frequency tables and bar charts to show the lengths of the names.
Children then use these to compare the lengths of the star names and the real names.

Further extension
Ask children to name their favourite stars. They use the internet to find out if their star names are their real names. If they have a different star name, is it longer or shorter than their real name? Children make frequency tables and bar charts to show this information. Does it show the trends or patterns children would expect to see?

Be aware	Outcomes
• This is an opportunity to ensure that children understand the need for appropriate scales and that, when comparing two sets of data, using different scales would be misleading.	• I can draw bar charts and frequency tables from sets of data. • I can use graphs and tables to help me answer questions about the data. • I can work out differences between amounts by subtracting or counting on.

Challenge Plan: Year 3

D2: adding/subtracting 10s; adding/subtracting 2-digit numbers; adding/subtracting 100s; adding/subtracting 9, 11, 19, 29

Summary

Y3 ⬡ **D2.1**   **Higher number squares**

Individuals, pairs or groups working independently

Year 3 Challenge Textbook page 43

Year 3 Challenge PCM 30

 Digit cards

Abacus Evolve objectives

- **Y4** Use known number facts and place value to add two 2-digit numbers, adding the tens first
- **Y4** Use known number facts and place value to subtract one 2-digit number from another, by counting on and back
- **Y4** Add near multiples of 10 to 2- and 3-digit numbers
- **Y4** Subtract near multiples of 10 from 2- and 3-digit numbers
- **Y4** Add and subtract 2- and 3-digit multiples of 10

Framework objectives

- **Y4** *Add or subtract mentally pairs of 2-digit whole numbers (e.g. 47 + 58, 91 − 35)*
- **Y4** Use knowledge of addition and subtraction facts and place value to derive sums and differences of pairs of multiples of 10, 100 or 1000

Teacher notes

Preparation
Photocopy PCM 30, one copy per child.

Getting started
Run through the example on the Textbook page, demonstrating how to find 723 + 30 = 753 using the 701–800 number square on the PCM.

Activity
Children work from Textbook page 43. They use the 701–800 square to solve addition and subtraction problems involving multiples of 10 and near multiples of 10. They then generate similar problems using digit cards.
Children use the same techniques to solve addition and subtraction problems using the 1201–1300 square, and again generate similar problems using digit cards.

Further extension
Children use the 701–800 and 1201–1300 squares. They explore adding and subtracting 500, and numbers just over and just under 500. This will involve children moving between the two number squares. For example 725 + 505 = 1230, and 1285 − 535 = 750.

Be aware

- This activity is a good opportunity to look out for and resolve any misunderstandings or misconceptions concerning place value.

Outcomes

- I can use a number square to help me add and subtract multiples of 10 from different numbers.
- I can make up my own calculations using digit cards.
- I can add numbers by adding the tens first and then the units. I can do the same for subtraction.

Supporting resources

There are more number square activities here, including 'Find 10 more than the target number' and 'Find 11 more than the target number':
- http://www.woodlands-junior.kent.sch.uk/maths/interactive/numbers.htm

Challenge Plan: Year 3

D2: adding/subtracting 10s; adding/subtracting 2-digit numbers; adding/subtracting 100s; adding/subtracting 9, 11, 19, 29

Summary

Y3 ☆ D2.2

Squares to zero

A small group working with an adult

Year 3 Challenge Textbook page 44

Year 3 Challenge PCM 31

Long thin strips of paper

Abacus Evolve objectives

- Add and subtract two 2-digit numbers, beginning to cross a multiple of 10
- Find a difference between two 2- or 3-digit numbers by counting on
- Use informal written methods to record subtractions for 2- and 3-digit numbers

Framework objectives

- *Add or subtract mentally combinations of 1-digit and 2-digit numbers*
- Develop and use written methods to record, support or explain addition and subtraction of 2-digit and 3-digit numbers
- Describe and explain methods, choices and solutions to puzzles and problems, orally and in writing, using pictures and diagrams

Teacher notes

Preparation
Photocopy PCM 31, at least one copy per child.

Activity
- Introduce the idea of finding the difference between the two numbers at the end of a line, and placing the answer at the mid-point of the line. Develop the idea using long strips of paper, folding them to find the middle. Children choose two numbers for the extremes, then place the difference at the mid-point; they then fold the halves in half and work out the two numbers at the new mid-points, and so on.
- Children work from Textbook page 44. The Textbook page develops this idea in the context of squares. Work through the first example together, using PCM 31. Ensure children understand that they need to find the differences, then join the mid-points to make a fresh square inside the first, and so on. The cycle continues until the four differences are all zero.
- Children choose four numbers in the range 0–50 and make their own squares on the PCM. When they are all at zero ask: *How many squares are there by this stage? Who has the most squares?*
- Children explore which starting numbers take the longest time to reach zero and investigate the maximum number of squares that can be obtained when the original four corner numbers are in the range 0–50.

Further extension
Children can explore triangles to zero. They will find that they cannot get to zero. What patterns do they notice in the numbers they end up with? How is it similar to squares to zero. How is it different?

If you have time
Children can repeat the investigation using numbers in the range 0–100, or 0–200.

Be aware

- The numbers in the square will always reach zero. If this does not happen, an arithmetical error has been made. This activity therefore promotes accuracy in calculation.

Outcomes

- I can subtract numbers up to 100 in my head or by writing.
- I can subtract numbers by counting on from one number to the other.

Supporting resources

Children can practise subtraction at:
- http://www.bbc.co.uk/skillswise/numbers/wholenumbers/addsubtract/mental/flash11.shtml

Challenge Plan: Year 3

D2: adding/subtracting 10s; adding/subtracting 2-digit numbers; adding/subtracting 100s; adding/subtracting 9, 11, 19, 29

Summary

Y3 ◇ **D2.3**

Addition walls

Pairs or groups working independently

Year 3 Challenge Textbook page 45

Year 3 Challenge PCM 32

Abacus Evolve objectives

- Add and subtract two 2-digit numbers, beginning to cross a multiple of 10
- Add a 2-digit number to a 2-, 3- or 4-digit number by partitioning into T and U then recombining
- Use informal written methods to record additions for 2- and 3-digit numbers
- Use informal written methods to record subtractions for 2- and 3-digit numbers
- Extend understanding that subtraction is the inverse of addition

Framework objectives

- *Add or subtract mentally combinations of 1-digit and 2-digit numbers*
- Develop and use written methods to record, support or explain addition and subtraction of 2-digit and 3-digit numbers
- Identify patterns and relationships involving numbers or shapes, and use these to solve problems
- Solve one-step and two-step problems involving numbers, money or measures, including time, choosing and carrying out appropriate calculations

Teacher notes

Preparation
Photocopy PCM 32, one copy per pair or group.

Getting started
Look together at the example addition number wall on the Textbook page. Discuss how to find the rule for completing it. *What are the missing numbers?* (60 and 100)

Activity
Children work from Textbook page 45 and record their answers on PCM 32. They complete three- and four-brick-base walls and devise walls of their own. Children then explore how the order of the base numbers of a four-brick-base wall affects the other numbers that are generated.

Further extension
Children work together to find some four-brick-base walls, with a top brick value of 20. *What is the total of the two outside bricks of the base? What is the total of the two inside bricks of the base? Is there a pattern?*

Be aware

- When children create addition wall puzzles for others to solve, they may not be aware that if they don't fill in enough of the numbers there will be more than one solution.

Outcomes

- I can add and subtract numbers up to 100 in my head and by writing sums.
- I can work in pairs and groups to solve number wall puzzles.
- I can use the way I solved the first number wall puzzle to help me to solve other ones.
- I can invent puzzles for my friends to do.

Supporting resources

Addition walls (here called pyramids) of various levels can be found at:
- http://www.amblesideprimary.com/ambleweb/mentalmaths/pyramid.html

Challenge Plan: Year 3

D2: adding/subtracting 10s; adding/subtracting 2-digit numbers; adding/subtracting 100s; adding/subtracting 9, 11, 19, 29

Summary

Y3 ⬡ D2.4

Hundreds and thousands linking cards

A small group working with an adult

Year 3 Challenge PCM 33

Thin card; place-value flashcards (optional)

Abacus Evolve objectives

- Add and subtract a multiple of 100 to and from a 4-digit number, crossing 1000
- Partition 3-digit numbers into H, T and U
- Know what each digit in a 3-digit number represents, including 0 as a place holder

Framework objectives

- *Add or subtract mentally combinations of 1-digit and 2-digit numbers*
- *Partition three-digit numbers into multiples of 100, 10 and 1 in different ways*

Teacher notes

Preparation
Photocopy PCM 33 onto thin A4 card and cut into 24 playing cards.

Activity
- Warm up with additions of multiples of 100 such as 1400 + 300 and 3100 + 700. You may wish to use place-value flashcards or ask children to make jottings of their answers and strategies.
- Give each child or pair a sub-set of six cards from PCM 33. (The cards in a sub-set are labelled A, B, C or D, and each sub-set is a complete chain.) Children arrange their cards in order to make a complete chain. The answer to the last card is shown on the first card.
- Children then work as a group to make a chain using all four sub-sets of cards.
- Shuffle the 24 cards together and deal them out. One child plays a card, then play passes to their left. If the next player has a card that answers the question on the first card (regardless of the sub-set), they play it; if they don't, they 'pass' and play continues to move to the left. The first player with no cards left is the winner.
- Note: For best results, the first card to be played should display the answer 1500 (there are four in the pack).

Further extension
Children can work with a partner to try and arrange any two of the sets of cards into a chain of 12 cards.

If you have time
Play the game again, but faster. Allow a 'play when you can go' rule, rather than asking children to take turns.

Be aware

- This activity can be used to check children's understanding of place value.

Outcomes

- I understand what each digit represents in a 4-digit number.
- I can add multiples of 100 in my head by adding the hundreds and then the thousands.
- I can use what I know about adding small numbers to help me add larger numbers.

Supporting resources

Children may enjoy the place-value game at:
- http://www.toonuniversity.com/flash.asp?err=496&engine=9

Challenge Plan: Year 3

D2: adding/subtracting 10s; adding/subtracting 2-digit numbers; adding/subtracting 100s; adding/subtracting 9, 11, 19, 29

Summary

Y3 ⭑ D2.5

Magic numbers

Pairs or groups working independently

Year 3 Challenge Textbook page 46

Year 3 Challenge PCM 34

Abacus Evolve objectives

- Add and subtract 9 and 11 to and from a 2- or 3-digit number
- Continue to recognise that addition can be done in any order
- Add several numbers by finding pairs that total 9, 10 or 11
- Know by heart addition and subtraction facts for pairs of numbers that total up to 20

Framework objectives

- *Add or subtract mentally combinations of 1-digit and 2-digit numbers*
- *Derive and recall all addition and subtraction facts for each number to 20, sums and differences of multiples of 10 and number pairs that total 100*
- Describe and explain methods, choices and solutions to puzzles and problems, orally and in writing, using pictures and diagrams

Teacher notes

Preparation
Photocopy PCM 34, at least one copy per pair or group.

Getting started
Together read about magic numbers on the Textbook page. Emphasise that it is important for each line of numbers to have the same total and that the total is the 'magic' number.

Activity
Children work from Textbook page 46 and record their answers on PCM 34. They complete the given five-pointed star and find the magic number. Children then complete three more magic stars using information and clues from the Textbook page.

Extra help
Provide children with counters numbered 1 to 12. Children can explore placing these in different places in the first star. Being able to move the numbers around should help children in solving the problem.

Further extension
Children choose a 1-digit number. They multiply all the numbers in one of their stars by that number. *What happens to the magic number?* Children try multiplying by other 1-digit numbers, and invetigate what happens to the magic number.

Be aware

- It is fine for children to use trial and error, but it is important that they develop a consistent method.

Outcomes

- I can add more than two numbers in my head.
- I can make notes to help me add and subtract more than two numbers.
- I can investigate different combinations of numbers in my magic star and find one that works.

Supporting resources

A magic square investigation can be found at:
- http://nrich.maths.org/public/viewer.php?obj_id=87

Challenge Plan: Year 3

D2: adding/subtracting 10s; adding/subtracting 2-digit numbers;
adding/subtracting 100s; adding/subtracting 9, 11, 19, 29

Summary

Y3 ⭐ D2.6   **Digital roots**

Individuals, pairs or groups working independently

Year 3 Challenge Textbook page 47

Year 3 Challenge PCM 35

Abacus Evolve objectives

- **Y4** Add near multiples of 10 to 2- and 3-digit numbers
- **Y4** Subtract near multiples of 10 from 2- and 3-digit numbers
- **Y4** Add or subtract 1, 10, 100 or 1000 to or from any integer
- **Y4** Recognise the relationship between Th, H, T and U

Framework objectives

- **Y4** *Add or subtract mentally pairs of 2-digit whole numbers (e.g. 47 + 58, 91 − 35)*
- **Y4** Partition, round and order 4-digit whole numbers; use positive and negative numbers in context and position them on a number line; state inequalities using the symbols < and >, e.g. −3 > −5, −1 < +1
- **Y4** Identify and use patterns, relationships and properties of numbers or shapes; investigate a statement involving numbers and test it with examples

Teacher notes

Getting started
Ask children to each write a 3-digit number. Together they explore the effect of adding 99 to each number, and the effect of subtracting 99 from each number. Children should find that adjusting by 1, then adding or subtracting 100, is effective every time (or adding or subtracting 100 first then adjusting by 1).

Activity
Children work from Textbook page 47. They explore the effect of adding or subtracting 99 to 3-digit numbers and record their answers on the table on PCM 35. They then find the digital roots of the 3-digit numbers, and explore the effect on the digital roots of adding and subtracting 99 and 98.
They then explore the effect on the digital roots of 4-digit numbers of adding or subtracting other near multiples of 10.

If you have time
Children could repeat the investigation using 2-digit or 4-digit numbers.

Be aware

- Children will need to record their work in an organised way. PCM 35 is designed to help with this.

Outcomes

- I can add 100 to any number.
- I can add 99 to any number by adding 100 and subtracting 1.
- I can investigate and spot patterns in numbers and calculations.

Supporting resources

The following pages include links to activities involving digital roots:
- http://www.teachingideas.co.uk/maths/nopdigital.htm
- http://nrich.maths.org/public/viewer.php?obj_id=5524

Challenge Plan: Year 3

E2: know 5 and 10 times-tables; division as inverse of multiplication; know 3 times-table; non-unit fractions of shapes and numbers

Summary

Y3 ○ E2.1

Multiplication linking cards

A small group working with an adult

Year 3 Challenge PCM 36

Thin card

Abacus Evolve objectives

- **Y4** Know by heart the multiplication facts for the 2, 3, 4, 5 and 10 times-tables
- **Y4** Derive division facts corresponding to the 2, 3, 4, 5 and 10 times-tables
- **Y4** Know the multiplication facts for the 6 times-table, and the corresponding division facts
- **Y4** Use doubling to find new facts from known facts
- **Y4** Begin to know the multiplication facts for the 9 times-table, and the corresponding division facts

Framework objectives

- **Y4** *Derive and recall multiplication facts up to 10 × 10, the corresponding division facts and multiples of numbers to 10 up to the tenth multiple*
- **Y4** *Respond appropriately to others in the light of alternative viewpoints*

Teacher notes

Preparation
Photocopy PCM 36 onto thin card and cut out the 24 playing cards.

Activity
- Warm up using multiplication and division in context, such as: *How many crews of 6 can you make with 42 rowers? What if there were 12 more rowers? If you have 84 rowers, how many crews of 6 would there be? 12 children have 3 marbles each. How many marbles are there altogether?* Encourage children to work together, drawing out multiplication and division facts and discussing ways of using known facts to derive answers.
- *What is 5 times 12?* Explain to children that two times-tables can be put together to make a higher times-table. For example, to multiply by 12, first multiply by 2, then by 10, and add the two products together.
- Give each child or pair a sub-set of six cards from PCM 36. (The cards in a sub-set are labelled A, B, C or D, and each sub-set is a complete chain.) Demonstrate the different question/answer sections on the cards. Children arrange the cards in order to make a complete chain. The answer to the question on the last card is on the first card.
- Children work as a group to make a chain using all four sub-sets of cards.
- Shuffle the 24 cards together and deal them out. One child plays a card, then play passes to their left. If the next player has a card that answers the question on the first card (regardless of the sub-set), they play it; if they don't, they 'pass' and play continues to move to the left. The first player with no cards left is the winner.
- Note: For best results, the first card to be played should display the answer 60 (there are four in the pack).

Further extension
Starting from selected known multiplication and division facts in the ×3 and ×6 tables, such as 3 × 9 = 27, lead children into creating a range of derived facts, such as 300 × 9 = 2700, 270 ÷ 30 = 9. *Using 3 × 9 = 27, how many calculations can you think of which have 9 as the answer?* Extend children as far as confidence allows, moving into thousands and amounts of money or measures.

Be aware

- Not all children grasp the inverse relationship between multiplication and division (i.e. because 9 × 3 = 27, therefore 27 ÷ 9 = 3). Support this idea with arrays.

Outcomes

- I can multiply and divide numbers by 2, 3, 4, 5, 6, 9 and 10.
- I can work out higher times-tables from the lower ones I know.
- I can use times-table facts to work out multiplication and division of larger numbers.

Supporting resources

A selection of different games to practise multiplication and division can be found at:
- http://www.fun4thebrain.com/

Challenge Plan: Year 3

E2: know 5 and 10 times-tables; division as inverse of multiplication; know 3 times-table; non-unit fractions of shapes and numbers

---

Summary

Y3 ⬡ E2.2

Ants and elephants

Pairs or groups working independently

Year 3 Challenge Textbook page 48

Year 3 Challenge PCM 37

Reference books on the natural world, the microscopic world, the solar system and deep space (optional); internet (optional)

Abacus Evolve objectives

- Recognise multiples of 10, 100 and 50
- Know by heart the multiplication facts for the 5 and 10 times-tables
- Derive division facts corresponding to the 5 and 10 times-tables
- Multiply by 10 and 100, shifting the digits 1 or 2 places to the left
- Rehearse division as the inverse of multiplication
- Extend use of patterns of similar calculations

Framework objectives

- Derive and recall multiplication facts for the 2, 3, 4, 5, 6 and 10 times-tables and the corresponding division facts; recognise multiples of 2, 5 or 10 up to 1000
- Multiply 1- and 2-digit numbers by 10 or 100, and describe the effect
- Understand that division is the inverse of multiplication and vice versa; use this to derive and record related multiplication and division number sentences
- Identify patterns and relationships involving numbers or shapes, and use these to solve problems

---

Teacher notes

Preparation
Photocopy PCM 37, one copy per pair or group.

Activity
Children work from Textbook page 48. They read about ants and elephants, as examples of very small and very big animals. Children then use PCM 37 to explore the range of sizes of animals and other living things, measured by length or height. They begin with ants (in the range 1–9 mm long) and, using the data provided on the PCM, find animals that are 10 times bigger than ants (i.e. in the range 1–9 cm). They then find animals that are 10 times bigger again, and so on. They then find animals that are 10 times smaller than ants, and animals 10 times smaller again.
As appropriate, make links between repeated multiplications of 10 (i.e. $10 \times 10 = 100$) and 10 times smaller being $\frac{1}{10}$. Children should begin to appreciate the effect of a scale factor, when applied repeatedly.

Further extension
Children choose two living things that they have explored. They say how many times bigger or smaller the living things are than each other. (Encourage answers such as 10 times, 100 times, 1000 times bigger or smaller.)

Be aware

- The common error of 'just add zero' when multiplying by 10 can cause confusion when dealing with decimals. Encourage children to discuss what really happens to the place value of individual digits, using a place-value grid for visual support if necessary.

Outcomes

- I can multiply numbers by 10 and explain what happens.
- I understand that division is the opposite of multiplication.
- I can compare the sizes of different creatures and record them in my table.

Supporting resources

Children can look here to research sizes of living things:
- http://www.guinnessworldrecords.com/records/natural_world/default.aspx (largest animal sizes)
- http://www.earthlife.net/insects/six01.html (insects)
- http://www.cellsalive.com/howbig.htm (measures smaller than 1 mm)

Challenge Plan: Year 3

E2: know 5 and 10 times-tables; division as inverse of multiplication; know 3 times-table; non-unit fractions of shapes and numbers

Summary

Y3 ◇ E2.3	**Missing-number multiplications and divisions**
	Individuals, pairs or groups working independently
	Year 3 Challenge Textbook page 49
	Digit cards

Abacus Evolve objectives

- Rehearse division as the inverse of multiplication
- Extend understanding that multiplication can be done in any order

Framework objectives

- Understand that division is the inverse of multiplication and vice versa; use this to derive and record related multiplication and division number sentences
- Solve one-step and two-step problems involving numbers, money or measures, including time, choosing and carrying out appropriate calculations
- Follow up others' points and show whether they agree or disagree in a whole-class discussion

Teacher notes

Activity

Children work from Textbook page 49. They work out the missing digits in three multiplications of 2-digit by 1-digit numbers.

They then explore other possibilities for completing multiplications in the form □□ × □ = □□ using three different digits as multipliers. They should find there are six possible combinations. They write out the products of their multiplications and see if a partner can work out the original three digits from the products. Encourage children to look at the units digits in the products to help guide their thinking when solving others' problems. (E.g. if none of the products ends in 0 or 5, then none of the digit cards is a 5.)

Children then solve similar division problems and complete some calculations to explore the relationship between multiplication and division as inverse operations.

Further extension

Ask children to invent other 2-digit by 1-digit multiplications using their digit cards. How many different products can they make between 40 and 60?

Be aware

- Not all children grasp the inverse relationship between multiplication and division (i.e. because $9 \times 3 = 27$, therefore $27 \div 9 = 3$). Support this idea with arrays.

Outcomes

- I can remember multiplication facts for the 2, 3, 4, 5, 6 and 10 times-tables.
- I can use times-table facts to help me divide numbers.
- I understand that dividing is the opposite of multiplying.
- I can arrange digit cards and find as many calculations as possible.

Supporting resources

There are lots of multiplication and division activities here:
- http://www.teachingideas.co.uk/maths/contents07multiplicationdivision.htm

Challenge Plan: Year 3

E2: know 5 and 10 times-tables; division as inverse of multiplication; know 3 times-table; non-unit fractions of shapes and numbers

Summary

Y3 ⭐ E2.4	**Multiples of 3, 6 and 9**
	Individuals, pairs or groups working independently
	Year 3 Challenge Textbook page 50
	Year 3 Challenge PCMs 3 and 30 (optional)
	Blue, black and red crayons

Abacus Evolve objectives

- Know by heart the multiplication facts for the 3 times-table
- Derive division facts corresponding to the 3 times-table
- Begin to know multiplication facts for the 6 times-table and corresponding division facts
- Extend use of patterns of similar calculations

Framework objectives

- Derive and recall multiplication facts for the 2, 3, 4, 5, 6 and 10 times-tables and the corresponding division facts; recognise multiples of 2, 5 or 10 up to 1000
- Identify patterns and relationships involving numbers or shapes, and use these to solve problems
- Develop and use specific vocabulary in different contexts

Teacher notes

Preparation
Photocopy PCM 3, one copy per child.
Photocopy PCM 30 for those children who are likely to reach the Extra activity on the Textbook page.

Getting started
Ask children to give examples of multiples of 3, 6 and 9, to check they are clear about these. Using a 1–100 square for reference, introduce the activity, explaining that children will be drawing coloured stripes on multiples of 3, 6 and 9 in blue, black and red, respectively. Pick out 12 and 18 and note that 12 will be both blue and black, and 18 will be coloured blue, black and red.

Activity
Children work from Textbook page 50. They use a 1–100 square from PCM 3 and colour the multiples of 3, 6 and 9 blue, black and red. They then investigate the patterns of coloured numbers with respect to which numbers have which multiples (e.g. 15 is only a multiple of 3 but 18 is a multiple of 3, 6 and 9).
Children then identify the multiples of 10 on the right of the square. They look at the colours of numbers that are 3 more and 3 less than 30, 60 and 90, and look for a pattern with regard to what their multiples are.

Information
If children consider the coloured numbers carefully they should notice that the digits of a multiple of 3, 6 or 9 always add up to a multiple of 3.

Be aware

- Children will need to be careful when drawing coloured stripes on the numbers, to make sure they leave enough space for other coloured stripes.

Outcomes

- I can identify multiples of 3, 6 and 9 using number squares.
- I can spot patterns in a 1–100 number square.

Supporting resources

This game involves identifying multiples of 10:
- http://www.oswego.org/ocsd-web/games/Ghostblasters1/gbcd.html

Children can shade selected multiples in different colours on this interactive 1–100 square:
- http://www.hellam.net/maths2000/100square.html

Try this multiples quiz:
- http://www.bbc.co.uk/skillswise/numbers/wholenumbers/whatarenumbers/multiplesandfactors/

E2: know 5 and 10 times-tables; division as inverse of multiplication; know 3 times-table; non-unit fractions of shapes and numbers

Summary

Y3 ⬡ E2.5	**Escape from 100**
	A small group working with an adult
	Year 3 Challenge Textbook page 51
	Year 3 Challenge PCMs 38 and 39
	1–100 square

◁|oo|▷ Abacus Evolve objectives

- Know by heart the multiplication facts for the 3 times-table
- Derive division facts corresponding to the 3 times-table
- Recognise odd and even numbers up to at least 100
- Know by heart doubles of numbers up to 20 and the corresponding halves
- Derive doubles of multiples of 5 up to 100 and the corresponding halves

Framework objectives

- Derive and recall multiplication facts for the 2, 3, 4, 5, 6 and 10 times-tables and the corresponding division facts; recognise multiples of 2, 5 or 10 up to 1000
- Use knowledge of number operations and corresponding inverses, including doubling and halving, to estimate and check calculations
- Identify patterns and relationships involving numbers or shapes, and use these to solve problems

T Teacher notes

Preparation
Photocopy PCMs 38 and 39 and 1–100 squares, one copy of each per child or pair.

Activity
- Ask some two-step mental calculation questions to get children used to the idea of using two-step rules. For example, for the rule ×3, +1, ask: *Think of a number, multiply it by 3, then add 1. If you input the number 5, what is the output?* (16) Give some outputs and see if children can work out the inputs.
- Children work from Textbook page 51. They start by finding outputs and inputs for the ×3, +1 rule.
- Then introduce the flowchart for Rule A on PCM 38 and explain how it works. Demonstrate inputting a small number through it. For different starting numbers, you will create strings of numbers that can eventually be joined up, and some numbers will produce a repeating loop. For example, starting with 5, the string of numbers is 5, 16, 8, 4, 2, 1. Starting with 1 the next number is 4, so the continuous loop of 4, 2 and 1 is formed once again. Starting with 6, the string is 6, 3, 10, 5, and this now joins up with the string when starting from 5.
- Children explore putting different numbers into the flowchart and see which 'escape' and which become trapped in loops. *Are there loops other than the 4, 2, 1 loop?*
- Repeat for the flowchart for Rule B on PCM 39.

Further extension
Children make a flowchart using these options: If a multiple of 3, then ×2, −1; if not a multiple of 3 and odd, then ×3, −1; if not a multiple of 3 and even, then ÷2, −1.

Information
In Rule A, odd numbers less than 33 will escape from the flowchart.

Be aware

- Children may not at first see that different numbers can lead them back into the same loop. Drawing the loops on the 100-square should make this more obvious.

Outcomes

- I can input numbers into a flowchart and work through the boxes to work out the output number.
- I can recognise odd and even numbers.
- I can recognise numbers that are in the 3 times-table.

Supporting resources

Children can use this online function machine:
- http://www.amblesideprimary.com/ambleweb/mentalmaths/functionmachines.html

E2: know 5 and 10 times-tables; division as inverse of multiplication; know 3 times-table; non-unit fractions of shapes and numbers

Summary

Y3 ☆ **E2.6**	**Fractions of quantities**
👤 👥 👪	Individuals, pairs or groups working independently
📖	Year 3 Challenge Textbook page 52
✂️	Linking cubes

Abacus Evolve objectives

- **Y4** Begin to relate fractions to division
- **Y4** Find fractions of numbers, quantities and shapes
- **Y4** Find quarters by halving halves
- **Y4** Derive division facts corresponding to the 2, 3, 4, 5 and 10 times tables

Framework objectives

- **Y4** Find fractions of numbers, quantities or shapes (e.g. $\frac{1}{5}$ of 30 plums, $\frac{3}{8}$ of a 6 by 4 rectangle)
- **Y4** *Derive and recall multiplication facts up to 10 × 10, the corresponding division facts and multiples of numbers to 10 up to the tenth multiple*
- **Y4** Solve one-step and two-step problems involving numbers, money or measures, including time; choose and carry out appropriate calculations, using calculator methods where appropriate

Teacher notes

Preparation
Prepare representations of the chocolate bars shown on Textbook page 52, using linking cubes.

Activity
Children work from Textbook page 52. They look at fractions of chocolate bars, and make up some of their own fractions. They can use the linking cube versions to confirm the fractions they have made. They move on to working out and comparing fractions of numbers, using the < and > symbols. They should work out the individual parts of each question first, and then compare them.
They then compare cash savings, e.g. which is the greater saving: $\frac{1}{3}$ off £6·99 or $\frac{2}{5}$ off £5·80?
The examples start with unit fractions, but move on to non-unit fractions. Children do not encounter improper fractions.

Extra help
Use arrays to support understanding of the connection between fractions and division.

Further extension
Ask children to find all the unit fractions of 36 they can think of that are whole numbers. Then ask them find all the non-unit fractions of 36 they can think of that are whole numbers.

Be aware

- Children may find this activity more challenging if they have not made the connection between fractions and division, particularly with non-unit fractions.

Outcomes

- I can work out fractions of numbers by dividing.
- I can use times-tables to help me divide.
- I can compare fractions of numbers and put them in order.
- I can work out fractions of money amounts.

A3: rounding 3-digit numbers; solving real-life problems involving money; adding 2-digit numbers to 2-, 3- and 4-digit numbers; adding near doubles

Summary

Y3 ⬡ **A3.1**

Rounding up and down

A small group working with an adult

Year 3 Challenge PCM 40

◁|∘∘|▷ Abacus Evolve objectives

- Round numbers less than 100 to the nearest 10
- Begin to round 3-digit numbers to the nearest 100 and 10
- Read weighing scales to the nearest labelled and unlabelled division

Framework objectives

- Round 2- or 3-digit numbers to the nearest 10 or 100 and give estimates for their sums and differences
- *Read, to the nearest division and half-division, scales that are numbered or partially numbered; use the information to measure and draw to a suitable degree of accuracy*
- Actively include and respond to all members of the group

T̄ Teacher notes

Preparation
Photocopy PCM 40 several times for yourself. On the first copy, mark the kangaroo hops, end numbers on number lines, and joey weights.

Activity
- Use the first section of PCM 40 as a warm-up to rounding. Mark the kangaroo jumps as 37 metres, 46 metres, 54 metres. Ask children to round each of these lengths to the nearest 10 metres. *How many (40 m) jumps will take the first kangaroo more than 200 metres?*
- Repeat with other lengths of jumps on other copies of the PCM.
- On the second section of the PCM, number the ends of the empty number lines with *10* and *50*, and *160* and *200*, respectively. Draw arrows pointing to some of the positions on the first line, e.g. the third, sixth and ninth intervals. Do not label them with their numbers.
- Discuss how to work out the size of the interval (4), then ask children to give the exact value of the positions marked.
- Ask children to round each of the values to the nearest 10. *Which whole numbers could round to 40? How many can you find?*
- Repeat for the 160–200 number line, and then for number lines with different end numbers on other copies of the PCM.
- Move on to interpreting partially numbered scales in the third section of PCM 40. Draw arrows to indicate the baby kangaroos' weights as about 342, 273 and 158 grams. Ask children to round the weights, first to the nearest 50 grams, then to the nearest 10 grams.
- *What do the three joeys' weights add up to?* Children use the weights rounded to 50 grams first, then the weights rounded to 10 grams. *What do you think of the difference between these?*
- Repeat with different weights on other copies of the PCM.

If you have time
Use the bottom section of PCM 40. In the empty question box write: *192 + 54*, and give the alternatives as: *A 190 + 50, B 190 + 60, C 200 + 50, D 200 + 60.* Children choose the nearest approximation.

Be aware

- Children may assume that intervals in partially numbered scales are always worth 1.

Outcomes

- I can round numbers to the nearest 10.
- I can use rounding to estimate calculations.
- I can read scales that don't have every division marked.

Supporting resources

There are more rounding practice activities here:
- http://www.higherbebington.wirral.sch.uk/games/rounders.html

Challenge Plan: Year 3

A3: rounding 3-digit numbers; solving real-life problems involving money; adding 2-digit numbers to 2-, 3- and 4-digit numbers; adding near doubles

Summary

Y3 ⬩ A3.2 — **Rounding and estimating**

Pairs or groups working independently

Year 3 Challenge Textbook page 53

Year 3 Challenge PCM 41

Calculators (optional)

Abacus Evolve objectives

- Round numbers less than 100 to the nearest 10
- Begin to round 3-digit numbers to the nearest 100 and 10
- Add and subtract a multiple of 10 to and from a 2-digit number, crossing 100 when adding
- Add and subtract a multiple of 10 to and from a 3-digit number, beginning to cross 100
- Understand and use £.p notation

Framework objectives

- Round 2-digit or 3-digit numbers to the nearest 10 or 100 and give estimates for their sums and differences
- *Add or subtract mentally combinations of 1- and 2-digit numbers*
- Solve one- and two-step problems involving numbers, money or measures, including time, choosing and carrying out appropriate calculations
- Use talk to organise roles and actions

Teacher notes

Preparation
Photocopy PCM 41, two or more copies per pair or group.

Activity
Children work from Textbook page 53. First they estimate answers to TU + TU additions by rounding each number to the nearest 10 before adding.
They repeat the activity rounding money amounts, first rounding them to the nearest pound before adding, then rounding to the nearest 10p.
Children then create HTU + TU calculations by selecting numbers from two sets. They round the individual numbers to the nearest 10, then add them. They repeat, but this time they find the differences between the pairs of numbers.
They repeat the addition and subtraction activities again, this time with money amounts, which they round to the nearest 10p.
Children should realise that when adding or subtracting the rounded numbers (multiples of 10), they can use TU + U facts they already know, e.g. 430 + 80 = 510, because 43 + 8 = 51.
Children play the estimating game on PCM 41. They take turns at being the Game Master, choosing pairs of numbers and whether to add or subtract (if only two children are playing, they each have two turns). The other children use rounding to estimate the lower and upper limits between which the exact answer will fall. They should aim to capture the answer in their range, but also try to make the range of their lower and upper limits as small as they can. The Game Master works out the exact answer, using a calculator if necessary, then they all check to see whose estimates were closest.

Be aware

- Ensure children understand how to apply known number facts to find answers to new calculations. For example 43 + 8 = 51 so 430 + 80 = 510, not 5100.

Outcomes

- I can round numbers to the nearest 10.
- I can round amounts of money to the nearest £1 and 10p.
- I can estimate an addition or subtraction by rounding the numbers first and then working it out.

Supporting resources

Try these estimation and rounding activities:
- http://www.mathsisfun.com/numbers/estimation-game.php
- http://pbskids.org/cyberchase/games/ballparkestimation/ballparkestimation.html

Challenge Plan: Year 3

A3: rounding 3-digit numbers; solving real-life problems involving money; adding 2-digit numbers to 2-, 3- and 4-digit numbers; adding near doubles

Summary

Y3 ⬠ A3.3

Take three numbers

Pairs or groups working independently

Year 3 Challenge Textbook page 54

Abacus Evolve objectives

- Add and subtract a multiple of 10 to and from a 3-digit number, beginning to cross 100
- Use informal written methods to record additions for 2- and 3-digit numbers
- Use informal written methods to record subtractions for 2- and 3-digit numbers
- Find a difference between two 2- or 3-digit numbers by counting on
- Extend understanding that subtraction is the inverse of addition

Framework objectives

- *Add or subtract mentally combinations of 1- and 2-digit numbers*
- Develop and use written methods to record, support or explain addition and subtraction of 2- and 3-digit numbers
- Follow a line of enquiry by deciding what information is important; make and use lists, tables and graphs to organise and interpret the information
- Identify patterns and relationships involving numbers or shapes, and use these to solve problems

Teacher notes

Activity

Children work from Textbook page 54. First, they choose two numbers from the three numbers given; they add the pair of numbers, they find the difference between them, then they add the sum and the difference. They repeat for the other possible pairs that can be made from the three numbers given. They should be looking for relationships between the numbers. The answers are:

581 + 465 = 1046	581 − 465 = 116	1046 + 116 = 1162
581 + 347 = 928	581 − 347 = 234	928 + 234 = 1162
465 + 347 = 812	465 − 347 = 118	812 + 118 = 930

They will find that:
- two of the subtractions add to the third (116 + 118 = 234)
- two of the final additions (i.e. adding the sum and the difference for the same pair) give the same number (1162), and this is double the largest of the original numbers (581)
- the third of the final additions gives a number (930) which is double the middle of the original numbers (465).

Children should discuss these patterns and see if they can work out why they occur.

Children then choose three numbers from a set of 3-digit multiples of 10, and they make these into the three possible pairs. For each pair they find the sum and the difference, and so produce two sets of three new numbers. For each new set, they repeat the exercise of finding sums and differences between pairs, and produce four new sets of numbers. As before they look for patterns and relationships between the numbers produced. They will find that the answers to the initial subtractions are repeated in the second set of subtractions. They repeat the activity, starting with a new set of three 3-digit multiples of 10.

If you have time

Children add the sums and differences they found between the three original pairs of 3-digit multiples of 10. What do they notice? (Two of the additions give the same answer, which is double the biggest original number; the third answer is double the middle number.)

Be aware

- Recording the investigation systematically, e.g. in tables, is a skill that may need support at this stage.

Outcomes

- I can add and subtract multiples of 10 in my head.
- I can investigate patterns of numbers.
- I can describe different patterns that I can see in numbers.

Challenge Plan: Year 3

A3: rounding 3-digit numbers; solving real-life problems involving money; adding 2-digit numbers to 2-, 3- and 4-digit numbers; adding near doubles

Summary

Y3 ⬡ **A3.4**

Fibonacci's pattern

Individuals, pairs or groups working independently

Year 3 Challenge Textbook page 55

 Abacus Evolve objectives

- Add a 1-digit number to a 2-digit number, bridging a multiple of 10
- Add and subtract two 2-digit numbers, beginning to cross a multiple of 10
- Add and subtract a 2-digit number to and from a 3-digit number
- Use informal written methods to record additions for 2- and 3-digit numbers
- Add a 2-digit number to a 2-, 3- or 4-digit number by partitioning into T and U then recombining
- Extend use of patterns of similar calculations

Framework objectives

- *Add or subtract mentally combinations of 1-digit and 2-digit numbers*
- Develop and use written methods to record, support or explain addition and subtraction of 2-digit and 3-digit numbers
- Represent the information in a puzzle or problem using numbers, images or diagrams; use these to find a solution and present it in context, where appropriate using £.p notation or units of measure
- Identify patterns and relationships involving numbers or shapes, and use these to solve problems

Teacher notes

Getting started
Use Textbook page 55 to introduce children to Fibonacci and his famous pattern.

Activity
Children work from Textbook page 55. They explore the numbers in the Fibonacci pattern as they continue to grow, taking the pattern up to at least 100.
They then create their own Fibonacci-style pattern, starting with a different pair of numbers.
Children then fill in the gaps in incomplete Fibonacci-style sequences.

Information
The Fibonacci pattern, going up to the first number beyond 100, is:
1, 1, 2, 3, 5, 8, 13, 21, 34, 55, 89, 144.

Extra help
To help children find the rule, ask them to look at any two 'next-door' numbers in the pattern, and add them together. *What do you notice?* Children should see that the total is the next number in the pattern.

Further extension
Ask children to think of a big 2-digit number, e.g. 64. *Subtract your number from 100* (36). Use these numbers to start a pattern: 100, 64, 36. Each time subtract the number from the number before it: 100, 64, 36, 28, 8. Stop when the numbers no longer decrease. Children think of different 2-digit numbers to subtract from 100 to make a pattern like this. *What is the longest pattern you can make?*

Be aware

- Children who move on to the Extra activity may not realise they can use what they know about even numbers and halving to check for multiples of 4. If half of 144 is even, then 144 is a multiple of 4.

Outcomes

- I can add 1- and 2-digit numbers in my head.
- I can spot patterns in sequences of numbers.
- I can continue patterns by working out what comes next.

Supporting resources

Information about Fibonacci and related activities:
- http://www.mcs.surrey.ac.uk/personal/r.knott/fibonacci/fibnat.html
- http://nrich.maths.org/public/viewer.php?obj_id=2468
- http://nrich.maths.org/public/viewer.php?obj_id=2470

Challenge Plan: Year 3

A3: rounding 3-digit numbers; solving real-life problems involving money; adding 2-digit numbers to 2-, 3- and 4-digit numbers; adding near doubles

Summary

Y3 ◇ **A3.5**

Think of a number

A small group working with an adult

Year 3 Challenge Textbook page 56

Digit cards 0–9; place value cards (Gattegno style, with overlaps)

Abacus Evolve objectives

- **Y4** Double or halve 2-digit numbers by doubling or halving the tens first
- **Y4** Derive doubles of integers up to 50 and the corresponding halves
- **Y4** Understand the principles (not the names) of the commutative and associative laws as they apply or not to addition and subtraction

Framework objectives

- **Y4** Identify the doubles of 2-digit numbers; use to calculate doubles of multiples of 10 and 100 and derive the corresponding halves
- **Y4** *Add or subtract mentally pairs of 2-digit whole numbers (e.g. 47 + 58, 91 − 35)*
- **Y4** Report solutions to puzzles and problems, giving explanations and reasoning orally and in writing, using diagrams and symbols
- **Y4** Respond appropriately to others in the light of alternative viewpoints

Teacher notes

Activity
- As a warm-up, lead children in a doubling exercise, by holding up digit cards and asking children to say the doubles. Move on to using place value cards to hold up 2-digit numbers. Then show children some even 2-digit numbers and ask them which numbers have been doubled to make them.
- Children work from Textbook page 56. They are shown a picture of a function machine that doubles numbers. First they work out the outputs of given input numbers. Then they work out inputs when given outputs.
- They move on to a two-step function machine (×2, +1). Eight numbers are given as a mixed collection of inputs and outputs. Children find the three pairs that go together, and for the unpaired numbers work out what their matching input/output could be.
- Children then devise their own two-step machines, combining addition/subtraction with doubling. They input five different numbers and find the outputs. From these they make a set of eight numbers (three pairs, two singles). They swap their function machines and sets of eight numbers with another member of the group, who tries to find the matching pairs of inputs and outputs and works out missing inputs/outputs for the unpaired numbers.

Further extension
Children devise two-step machines and sets of mixed inputs and outputs as before, but when they swap with a partner, they only swap mixed sets of numbers. Can the partner work out the functions as well as pair up and complete inputs and outputs?

Be aware

- Children may understand that they need to use inverse operations to work backwards, but may not realise they need to do the operations in the reverse order as well (i.e. ×2, +1 is solved by doing −1, ÷2 and not ÷2, −1)

Outcomes

- I understand that subtraction is the opposite of addition.
- I understand that halving is the opposite of doubling.
- I can work out what number will come out of a two-step function machine.
- I can work backwards to find out what number went into a function machine if I know what came out.

Supporting resources

Use this online function machine:
- http://www.amblesideprimary.com/ambleweb/mentalmaths/functionmachines.html
Try this function machine-type investigation:
- http://nrich.maths.org/public/viewer.php?obj_id=5576

Challenge Plan: Year 3

A3: rounding 3-digit numbers; solving real-life problems involving money; adding 2-digit numbers to 2-, 3- and 4-digit numbers; adding near doubles

Summary

Y3 ⟡ A3.6

Four square

Individuals, pairs or groups working independently

Year 3 Challenge Textbook page 57

1 cm² square dotted paper

Abacus Evolve objectives

- **Y4** Derive doubles of integers up to 50 and the corresponding halves
- **Y4** Use doubling or halving to find new facts from known facts
- **Y4** Understand area as 'covering' in two dimensions
- **Y4** Measure area using standard units: square centimetres

Framework objectives

- **Y4** Identify the doubles of 2-digit numbers; use to calculate doubles of multiples of 10 and 100 and derive the corresponding halves
- **Y4** Draw rectangles and measure and calculate their perimeters, find the area of rectilinear shapes drawn on a square grid by counting squares
- **Y4** Solve one- and two-step problems involving numbers, money or measures, including time; choose and carry out appropriate calculations, using calculator methods where appropriate

Teacher notes

Activity
Children work from Textbook page 57. They follow the instructions to draw a square on dotted paper, beginning with a single line drawn at an angle. They recognise the alternative possibilities.

They explore drawing squares of different sizes on dotted paper. Children move on to finding the area of their squares. The method on the Textbook page illustrates enclosing the tilted square in a larger square whose area can be found easily by counting squares. This leaves four identical triangles between the tilted square and the larger square. Children should be able to work out the area of one triangle by finding the area of the rectangle it sits within and halving. They should then be able to work out the area of all four triangles by doubling and doubling again. The area of the tilted square can then be found by subtracting the area of all four triangles from the area of the larger square.

Children are then challenged to make squares of specific areas. They should look for patterns between the side lengths of the triangles and the sides of the larger surrounding square.

Extra help
Children can start by finding squares with sides at 45° angles. This should make it easy to see that the area of the square will be exactly half of the square that surrounds it.

Further extension
Children draw right-angled triangle on dotted paper. They then draw three more identical triangles so that the four triangles surround a square, for example like this:

Children use what they have learned to find the area of the shape they have drawn.

Be aware

- Some children may not be completely familiar with the concept of area. Where necessary, support them in understanding and calculating area.

Outcomes

- I can work out the area of a square by counting the number of squares it covers.
- I can work out the area of four identical triangles by doubling the area of one of them twice.
- I can draw squares of given areas on dot paper.

Supporting resources

This online tool allows exploration of area by counting:
- http://www.shodor.org/interactivate/activities/areaexplorer

Challenge Plan: Year 3

B3: odd and even numbers, and counting in 5s and 50s; multiplication facts for the 4 times-table; right-angled turns; compass directions

Summary

Y3 **B3.1**   Doubling, doubling and doubling

A small group working with an adult

 Year 3 Challenge PCM 42

∘∘∘◁ Abacus Evolve objectives

- **Y4** Derive doubles of integers up to 50 and the corresponding halves
- **Y4** Double or halve 2-digit numbers by doubling or halving the tens first
- **Y4** Use doubling or halving to find new facts from known facts
- **Y4** Begin to know the multiplication facts for the 8 times-table, and the corresponding division facts
- **Y4** Recognise odd and even numbers up to 1000

Framework objectives

- **Y4** Identify the doubles of 2-digit numbers; use these to calculate doubles of multiples of 10 and 100 and derive the corresponding halves
- **Y4** *Derive and recall multiplication facts up to 10 × 10, the corresponding division facts and multiples of numbers to 10 up to the tenth multiple*
- **Y4** Identify and use patterns, relationships and properties of numbers or shapes; investigate a statement involving numbers and test it with examples
- **Y4** Respond appropriately to others in the light of alternative viewpoints

⊤ Teacher notes

Preparation
Photocopy PCM 42, one copy per child or pair. If possible, enlarge the table at the top to help introduce the activity. Cut up the number cards at the bottom.

Activity
- Warm up by doubling some numbers (up to 20 or so). *What do you notice about all the doubles?* (They are all even; they are all multiples of 2.) *What do you notice when you double an even number?* (The double is a multiple of 4.)
- Use the top part of PCM 42 to demonstrate the activity and how to complete the table. Explain that children will be doubling the numbers 1 to 15 and writing the answers in the first column (×2). They will double these numbers again and write the answers in the next column (×4), and double these again to complete the ×8 column. (They could use the last column to show ×16 if you wish to continue the activity.)
- Check that children understand the relationship between repeated doubling and ×2, ×4 and ×8. Children complete the table on the PCM and discuss their results, cross-checking to make sure that any errors are not perpetuated.
- When they have completed this task, use the table to ask questions, initially simple ones and then trickier ones involving division. *What is 9 times 8? What is 13 times 4? What is 96 divided by 8?*
- Children work on the second section of the PCM, which is a set of 10 multiplications by 4 and 8. These involve larger numbers, and children will need to apply their repeated doubling strategy to solve them.

If you have time
The bottom section of PCM 42 consists of 20 numbers to cut out. Ask children to find matching pairs where one number is 4 or 8 times the other. They record the pairs as divisions, e.g. *84 ÷ 4 = 21*.

Be aware

- Children may be surprised by how large numbers become with repeated doubling, and assume that they have calculated incorrectly. Reassure where necessary.

Outcomes

- I can recognise even numbers.
- I can multiply by 4 by doubling and doubling again.
- I can divide by 4 by halving and halving again.
- I can use these ideas to help me multiply and divide by 8.

Supporting resources

Try this doubling and halving game:
- http://www.wmnet.org.uk/wmnet/custom/files_uploaded/uploaded_resources/852/2ring-centrev4.swf

Challenge Plan: Year 3

B3: odd and even numbers, and counting in 5s and 50s; multiplication facts for the 4 times-table; right-angled turns; compass directions

Summary

Y3 ⬡ B3.2

Multiplication and division cross-number puzzles

Individuals, pairs or groups working independently

Year 3 Challenge Textbook page 58

Year 3 Challenge PCM 43

1 cm squared paper (optional)

Abacus Evolve objectives

- Know by heart the multiplication facts for the 4 times-table
- Derive division facts corresponding to the 4 times-table
- Derive doubles of multiples of 5 up to 100 and the corresponding halves
- Derive doubles of multiples of 50 up to 500 and the corresponding halves
- Use doubling to find new facts (×4) from known facts (×2)

Framework objectives

- Derive and recall multiplication facts for the 2, 3, 4, 5, 6 and 10 times-tables and the corresponding division facts; recognise multiples of 2, 5 or 10 up to 1000
- Use knowledge of number operations and corresponding inverses, including doubling and halving, to estimate and check calculations
- Actively include and respond to all members of the group

Teacher notes

Preparation
Photocopy PCM 43, one copy per child or pair.

Activity
Children work from Textbook page 58. They use the clues on the Textbook page to solve and complete the first two cross-number puzzles on PCM 43. Then they work in pairs to devise their own clues for the third cross-number puzzle on the PCM. They should use the doubling facts they know to work out ×4 and ×8 and related divisions.

Extra help
Give children a simple table with four columns, headed *Number, doubled (×2), Doubled again (×4)* and *Doubled again (×8)*. Children choose some one digit numbers to enter into the table, to practise repeated doubling, and therefore multiplying by 4 and 8.

Further extension
Children work in pairs to design their own cross number puzzle on 1 cm squared paper. They should take care to label the grid correctly, considering which numbers they will need to write clues for.

Be aware

- Children may need to be reminded that they can use known doubling facts to break all the calculations down into simpler steps, and they do not need to find the answers from scratch.

Outcomes

- I can multiply by 4 by doubling and doubling again.
- I can divide by 4 by halving and halving again.
- I can use the same ideas to work out how to multiply and divide by 8.
- I can solve a cross-number puzzle.
- I can invent my own cross-number puzzle.

Supporting resources

Children can generate cross-number puzzles online:
- http://www.worksheetworks.com/puzzles/crossnumber.html

B3: odd and even numbers, and counting in 5s and 50s; multiplication facts for the 4 times-table; right-angled turns; compass directions

Summary

Y3 ⭐ B3.3

Centres of enlargement

Individuals, pairs or groups working independently

Year 3 Challenge Textbook page 59

Year 3 Challenge PCM 44

$1\,cm^2$ or $2\,cm^2$ squared paper

Abacus Evolve objectives

- Know by heart the multiplication facts for the 4 times-table
- Know by heart doubles of numbers up to 20 and the corresponding halves
- Use doubling to find new facts (×4) from known facts (×2)
- Use a ruler to draw and measure lines to the nearest half centimetre

Framework objectives

- Derive and recall multiplication facts for the 2, 3, 4, 5, 6 and 10 times-tables and the corresponding division facts; recognise multiples of 2, 5 or 10 up to 1000
- Use knowledge of number operations and corresponding inverses, including doubling and halving, to estimate and check calculations
- *Read, to the nearest division and half-division, scales that are numbered or partially numbered; use the information to measure and draw to a suitable degree of accuracy*

Teacher notes

Preparation
Photocopy PCM 44, one copy per child, pair or group.

Activity
Children work from Textbook page 59. The concept of enlargement is introduced by showing the same picture at different sizes.
The Textbook page then illustrates using a centre of enlargement as a method of enlarging a shape. Draw lines from a single point outside the shape to the shape's corners. Then extend those lines and double them. New points are found and can be joined to construct the enlarged shape whose sides are double the length of those of the original shape. The Textbook page explains that when the sides of a shape are doubled, the scale factor is ×2.
Children apply this method of enlargement to the shape on PCM 44 as a test piece before then going on to draw and enlarge their own shapes on squared paper, exploring ×2 and other scale factors.

Extra help
Use a photocopier to photocopy a picture at 100% and then at 200%. Ask children to compare the two copies. *How are they the same? How are they different?*

If you have time
Investigate halving the side lengths to produce reductions (and scale factors < 1).

Be aware

- Make sure that children recognise that the amount by which they increase the length of lines from the points is directly related to the scale factor of the new shape.

Outcomes

- I can recognise, describe and draw different 2D shapes.
- I can enlarge shapes by multiplying their sides by 2, 3 or 4.
- I can draw the enlargements of the shapes.

Supporting resources

This interactive site demonstrates enlargement:
- http://www.ngfl-cymru.org.uk/vtc/ngfl/maths/echalk/enlargement/index.htm

Challenge Plan: Year 3

B3: odd and even numbers, and counting in 5s and 50s; multiplication facts for the 4 times-table; right-angled turns; compass directions

---

Summary

Y3 **B3.4**

Hands on a clock

 A small group working with an adult

Year 3 Challenge Textbook page 60

Clock with movable hands; calculators (optional)

Abacus Evolve objectives

- **Y4** Begin to know that angles are measured in degrees
- **Y4** Recognise the relationship between degrees and right angles
- **Y4** Read the time to the nearest minute on analogue clocks

Framework objectives

- **Y4** *Know that angles are measured in degrees and that one whole turn is 360°; draw, compare and order angles less than 180°*
- **Y4** Read time to the nearest minute; use am, pm and 12-hour clock notation; choose units of time to measure time intervals; calculate time intervals from clocks and timetables
- **Y4** Report solutions to puzzles and problems, giving explanations and reasoning orally and in writing, using diagrams and symbols
- **Y4** Respond appropriately to others in the light of alternative viewpoints

---

Teacher notes

Activity

- Demonstrate the concept of turn using the movable hands on a clock, beginning with the whole turn made by the hour hand during 12 hours. Discuss half and quarter turns, and their relationship to right angles. Introduce degrees as the unit used to measure angle.
- Children work from Textbook page 60. First they use the information that 1 right angle = 90° to work out the angles through which the hour hand has turned on pairs of clocks. Encourage children to realise that one-third of 90° is 30° and so multiples of 30° are needed for whole hours, while half an hour is 15° and 20 minutes is 10°.
- Then move on to working out the angle through which the minute hand turns on a clock, using the information that the minute hand makes a whole turn in an hour. Some of the times on the Textbook page are straightforward fractions of a full turn, but others are trickier, requiring children to first work out that the angle for each 5 minutes is 30°, and then use this information.

Further extension

How many degrees does the minute hand turn in one minute? (6°). *How many seconds does it take for the minute hand to turn 1°?* (10 seconds).

Be aware

- Children may understand that in 15 minutes the minute hand turns a right angle, but may initially need support to work out what each 5 minutes is in degrees.

Outcomes

- I know that 360° is a full turn and 90° is a quarter of a turn.
- I can read clocks and work out the difference between two times.
- I can work out the angle the minute hand turns between different times.

Supporting resources

Explore right angles and degrees in clock times here:
- http://nrich.maths.org/public/viewer.php?obj_id=1159
- http://nrich.maths.org/public/viewer.php?obj_id=2814

Challenge Plan: Year 3

B3: odd and even numbers, and counting in 5s and 50s; multiplication facts for the 4 times-table; right-angled turns; compass directions

Summary

Y3 ○ B3.5

Routes around shapes

Individuals, pairs or groups working independently

Year 3 Challenge Textbook page 61

Year 3 Challenge PCM 45

1 cm² and 2 cm² square dot grid paper

Abacus Evolve objectives

- Recognise and use the four compass directions N, S, E, W
- Describe a route using distance and direction
- Make and describe right-angled turns between the four compass points
- Identify right angles in 2D shapes and the environment
- Make and describe right-angled turns
- Compare angles with a right angle

Framework objectives

- Read and record the vocabulary of position, direction and movement, using the four compass directions to describe movement about a grid
- Use a set-square to draw right angles and to identify right angles in 2D shapes; compare angles with a right angle; recognise that a straight line is equivalent to two right angles
- Follow a line of enquiry by deciding what information is important; make and use lists, tables and graphs to organise and interpret the information
- Explain a process or present information, ensuring items are clearly sequenced, relevant details are included and accounts ended effectively

Teacher notes

Preparation
Photocopy PCM 45, one copy per child or pair. (Set aside the right-hand section which is needed for Activity B3.6.)

Activity
Children work from Textbook page 61. They are introduced to the idea of describing the route around the edge of a shape using the eight compass directions. They learn that all the internal angles are multiples of $\frac{1}{2}$ a right angle.
Children practise describing the route around a shape using compass directions, and list its internal angles as numbers of right angles. They then repeat for the three shapes on PCM 45, and record the information in a table.
They move on to exploring other shapes that can be drawn on a 16-dot grid. They draw shapes on square dotted paper, and record the main features: number of sides, route around the shape given as compass directions, internal angles, and area if they can.

Further extension
Ask children to follow one of their sets of instructions in reverse order. *What shape do you get now?*

Be aware

- Children may need support to record the features of shapes systematically in a table.

Outcomes

- I can describe the route around the edge of a shape using compass directions.
- I can recognise right angles and half right angles in shapes.
- I can draw a table and record information in it.

Supporting resources

Children can draw shapes on this virtual pinboard:
- http://www.crickweb.co.uk/assets/resources/flash.php?&file=vpinboard4

This online game involves turning in 90°, 180° and 270°:
- http://www.bnsc.gov.uk/5265.aspx

Challenge Plan: Year 3

B3: odd and even numbers, and counting in 5s and 50s; multiplication facts for the 4 times-table; right-angled turns; compass directions

Summary

Y3 B3.6

Mathematical worms

Individuals, pairs or groups working independently

Year 3 Challenge Textbook page 62

Year 3 Challenge PCM 45

1 cm^2 or 2 cm^2 square dot paper

Abacus Evolve objectives

- Recognise and use the four compass directions N, S, E, W
- Describe a route using distance and direction
- Make and describe right-angled turns between the four compass points

Framework objectives

- Read and record the vocabulary of position, direction and movement, using the four compass directions to describe movement about a grid
- Identify patterns and relationships involving numbers or shapes, and use these to solve problems
- Describe and explain methods, choices and solutions to puzzles and problems, orally and in writing, using pictures and diagrams
- Develop and use specific vocabulary in different contexts

Teacher notes

Preparation
Photocopy PCM 45, one copy per child, pair or group. (You may have already photocopied PCM 45 for Activity B3.5, and set aside the right-hand section for this activity.)

Activity
Children work from Textbook page 62. They learn about fossilised worm tracks. The tracks are modelled mathematically using rules described in terms of the number of moves in one direction before making a clockwise turn.
Children deduce the rules of the tracks on PCM 45.
Then they explore drawing tracks of given rules on square dot paper, looking for similarities between tracks. They should notice that since a rule is applied repeatedly, it doesn't matter whether a rule is given as, for example, [3, 2, 4] or [2, 4, 3]; if the numbers in the rule are the same, they will produce the same track.

Further extension
Children can explore drawing the tracks on triangle dot paper. After they have moved forward, there is a 45° turn, rather than a 90° turn. *How does this change the shape that you make?*

If you have time
Children can explore making tracks that follow rules which involve anti-clockwise turns instead of clockwise turns.

Information
If children investigate worm tracks on the internet, they will find that models for tracks generally use a triangular grid, not a square one.

Be aware

- It may be helpful for children to orientate the page as they draw their tracks, to make sure their worm is turning in the right direction each time.

Outcomes

- I can use dot paper to draw different worm tracks.
- I can record the worm tracks using sets of numbers.
- I can describe worm tracks using compass directions.

Challenge Plan: Year 3

C3: locating positions on a grid; measuring and comparing weights; using units of time; sorting data using Venn and Carroll diagrams

Summary

Y3 ⭐ C3.1   **British cities**

Individuals, pairs or groups working independently

Year 3 Challenge Textbook page 63

Year 3 Challenge PCMs 46 and 47

Maps of Britain; calculators (optional); 20 cm × 20 cm squares drawn on 1 cm² paper made into 4 × 4 grids (optional)

Abacus Evolve objectives	Framework objectives
• Locate position on a grid with the rows and columns labelled • Recognise and use the four compass directions N, S, E, W	• Read and record the vocabulary of position, direction and movement, using the four compass directions to describe movement about a grid • Develop and use specific vocabulary in different contexts

Teacher notes

Preparation
Photocopy PCMs 46 and 47, one copy per child, pair or group.

Getting started
Look together at a map of Britain and discuss how to find specific locations. Invite answers related to grid references.

Activity
Children work from Textbook page 63. They are introduced to the letter/number system of grid referencing using the map of Britain on PCM 46. The map uses a grid of 100 km squares. To begin with, children label the columns and rows with letters and numbers. Once they have done this, they identify the grid references of the four capital cities that are labelled, to check their understanding of the referencing system. They write the grid references in the table on PCM 47.
Children use maps to identify and label the other cities shown on PCM 46, and continue to record answers in the table. They then locate the other cities listed in the table on the map, mark and label them, and record their locations.
Children move on to finding grid squares with more than one city marked. For each of these, they add the populations of cities in the same square, using calculators if needed.

Further extension
Children name a few small places in Britain that they know (for example places that they have relatives, or places they have been on holiday). They look them up on the internet and estimate where they are on the map. *What is the grid reference?*

Be aware	Outcomes
• Children may be able to label the grid accurately but may then be unsure how to read the grid references. Remind them to read the column number first, then the row number for example A1 rather than 1A.	• I can describe where places are on a map using letter and number codes. • I can find the locations of cities in Britain and place them on a map.

C3: locating positions on a grid; measuring and comparing weights; using units of time; sorting data using Venn and Carroll diagrams

Summary

Y3 ⬡ **C3.2**   **Map of Jersey**

A small group working with an adult

Year 3 Challenge PCMs 48 and 49

Demonstration-sized 20 × 20 grid with columns/rows labelled with letters/numbers; 20 cm × 20 cm grids drawn on 1 cm² paper (optional)

Abacus Evolve objectives

- **Y4** Locate position on a grid, based on labelling the horizontal and vertical lines
- **Y4** Begin to use the term 'coordinate'
- **Y4** Recognise simple examples of horizontal and vertical lines

Framework objectives

- **Y4** Recognise horizontal and vertical lines; use the eight compass points to describe direction; describe and identify the position of a square on a grid of squares
- **Y4** Respond appropriately to others in the light of alternative viewpoints

Teacher notes

Preparation
Photocopy PCMs 48 and 49, one copy per child or pair; enlarge a copy of PCM 49 for demonstration purposes. Make copies of simple 20 cm × 20 cm grids drawn on 1 cm² paper.

Activity
- Start by introducing a demonstration-sized 20 × 20 square grid with columns and rows labelled with letters and numbers, respectively. Check that children can interpret and find grid references correctly.
- Children work from PCM 48. They look at a pixellated outline map of Jersey. First, children label the grid, using letters for columns and numbers for rows. Then they work out the grid references of the shaded cells forming the outline, beginning with A10 and moving clockwise around the map.
- PCM 49 shows a map of Jersey on a Cartesian grid. Using the enlarged copy of the PCM, explain the difference between the two types of grid, establishing the following points.
  - On a Cartesian grid, the lines are labelled, not the columns and rows.
  - Numbers are used to label both vertical and horizontal lines.
  - Grid references are called coordinates and are shown as (x, y) where x is the horizontal axis and y is the vertical axis.
  - Coordinates describe points where vertical and horizontal lines cross or intersect.
- Ask questions to check children understand how to interpret and use the Cartesian grid.
- Children then identify the coordinates of the four places highlighted on the map.

Further extension
Children use simple 20 × 20 grids to create their own pixellated outline map and then redraw it on a Cartesian grid.

Be aware

- The step between grid references to coordinate references is not straightforward, so encourage children to discuss their ideas.

Outcomes

- I can find places on a grid using their grid references.
- I can write grid references to match features on a grid.
- I can use and read coordinates.

Supporting resources

Children can practise locating points from coordinates with this game:
- http://www.primaryresources.co.uk/online/coordinates.swf

Challenge Plan: Year 3

C3: locating positions on a grid; measuring and comparing weights; using units of time; sorting data using Venn and Carroll diagrams

Summary

Y3 ◇ C3.3

Ant and elephant weights

Individuals, pairs or groups working independently

Year 3 Challenge Textbook page 64

Reference books on the natural and microscopic worlds, or internet access

Abacus Evolve objectives

- Measure and compare weights using standard units: kilograms, grams
- Know the relationship between kilograms and grams
- Multiply by 10 and 100, shifting the digits 1 or 2 places to the left
- Rehearse division as the inverse of multiplication

Framework objectives

- Know the relationships between kilometres and metres, metres and centimetres, kilograms and grams, litres and millilitres; choose and use appropriate units to estimate, measure and record measurements
- Multiply 1-digit and 2-digit numbers by 10 or 100, and describe the effect
- Understand that division is the inverse of multiplication and vice versa; use this to derive and record related multiplication and division number sentences
- Follow a line of enquiry by deciding what information is important; make and use lists, tables and graphs to organise and interpret the information

Teacher notes

Getting started

Look at the table on Textbook page 64 with the group and discuss the relationship between the different rows, establishing that the range of weights in each row is 10 times the size of the one above. Check that children understand the different units and can convert between these as needed.

Activity

Children work from Textbook page 64. They read about the relative weights of ants and elephants.

They copy the table on the Textbook page, and complete it using reference books or the internet to find animals that fall into the different weight ranges. They begin with finding animals that are 10 times as heavy as an ant, and then 10 times as heavy again, until they reach the weight of an elephant. In this way they should begin to appreciate the cumulative effect of repeatedly multiplying or dividing weights by 10.

Be aware

- The common error of 'just add zero' when multiplying by 10 can cause confusion when dealing with decimals. Encourage children to discuss what really happens to the place value of individual digits, using a place-value grid for visual support if necessary.

Outcomes

- I can multiply numbers by 10 and explain what happens.
- I understand that division is the opposite of multiplication.
- I can research the weights of different animals, and record them in a table.

Supporting resources

This linking card game uses ×10 and ×100:
- http://www.primaryresources.co.uk/maths/x10x100.htm

This quiz practises multiplying and dividing by 10, 100, 1000:
- http://www.bbc.co.uk/skillswise/numbers/wholenumbers/multiplication/multiply10and100/quiz.shtml

Challenge Plan: Year 3

C3: locating positions on a grid; measuring and comparing weights; using units of time; sorting data using Venn and Carroll diagrams

Summary

Y3 C3.4

Time facts

Groups working independently

Year 3 Challenge Textbook page 65

Year 3 Challenge PCM 50

Thin card

Abacus Evolve objectives

- Use units of time and know the relationship between them: days, hours, minutes, seconds
- Use units of time and know the relationship between them: years, months, weeks, days, hours

Framework objectives

- Read the time on a 12-hour digital clock and to the nearest 5 minutes on an analogue clock; calculate time intervals and find start or end times for a given time interval
- Actively include and respond to all members of the group

Teacher notes

Preparation
Photocopy PCM 50 onto thin card and cut out the set of playing cards.

Getting started
Look at Textbook page 65 with the group and discuss the periods of time shown at the top. Ask questions about related periods of time, for example: *How many seconds in one minute?*
Quickly explain how to use the playing cards from PCM 50.

Activity
Children work from Textbook page 65. First they answer questions based on the relationship between pairs of units of time. For example: *How many days are there in a fortnight?*
Then they make other pairs from the units of time shown on the Textbook page and describe how they are related.
They then use the cards from PCM 50. They work as a group to arrange all 24 cards in a complete loop, in which the question on each card is answered on the next card.

Extra help
Together write out the units of time from the Textbook page in order from smallest to greatest.

Further extension
Give each child a set of cards; A, B, C or D. Children shuffle them, and then try to arrange them into correct chain as quickly as they can. The fastest child is the winner.

Be aware

- Because the metric system of measures is based on powers of 10, and times such as 3·45 can look like a decimal, children may wrongly think that units of time are also metric, and think, for example, that there are 100 minutes in 1 hour.

Outcomes

- I understand how years, months, weeks, days and hours, minutes and seconds are related.
- I can quickly change between different units of time.

Supporting resources

Game involving units of time:
- http://www.bbc.co.uk/education/dynamo/den/matching/index.htm

Calculate how old you are in different time units:
- http://www.mathcats.com/explore/age/calculator.html

Challenge Plan: Year 3

C3: locating positions on a grid; measuring and comparing weights; using units of time; sorting data using Venn and Carroll diagrams

Summary

Y3 ◌ C3.5

Calendars

A small group working with an adult

Year 3 Challenge Textbook page 66

Range of calendars showing this year and next; calculators

Abacus Evolve objectives

- **Y4** Use a calendar
- **Y4** Recognise and extend number sequences formed by counting from any number in steps of constant size, extending beyond zero when counting back
- **Y4** Begin to know the multiplication facts for the 7 times-table, and the corresponding division facts

Framework objectives

- **Y4** Read time to the nearest minute; use am, pm and 12-hour clock notation; choose units of time to measure time intervals; calculate time intervals from clocks and timetables
- **Y4** Recognise and continue number sequences formed by counting on or back in steps of constant size
- **Y4** *Derive and recall multiplication facts up to 10 × 10, the corresponding division facts and multiples of numbers to 10 up to the tenth multiple*
- **Y4** Identify and use patterns, relationships and properties of numbers or shapes; investigate a statement involving numbers and test it with examples

Teacher notes

Activity
- Read the rhyme *Thirty days hath September* together, looking at Textbook page 66.
- Ask questions to reinforce the number of days in each month. *How many days in August? Starting with August, what are the names of every second month up to December? Starting with January, what are the names of every second month up to May? What do you notice?* (August, October and December all have 31 days; January, March and May all have 31 days.)
- Discuss seasons, and which months are in each season.
- Give children a range of calendars to compare. Discuss different ways of presenting months and days, and look at patterns in days and dates across months in the same year and, if possible, across different years.
- Children work from Textbook page 66. Using a current calendar, they find the day that will occur most often during the year. (For a non-leap year, this will be the day on which both New Year's Day and New Year's Eve fall.)

- They then look for patterns in the numbering of days in different months. (In a non-leap year, January and October are the only months with the same number of days that start on the same day.) Encourage children to realise that, unless a leap year must be accounted for, any date will fall one day later the following year.
- Discuss the 'add 7' pattern that describes the sequence of dates for each day in the same month.
- Children then choose a block of four numbers from one month, multiply them diagonally and find the difference between the products. They will find the difference is 7, regardless of which block of four numbers they use. Can they explain why?

Be aware

- Children may not be familiar with the rhyme *Thirty days hath September* or they may know a different version (the Leapzine website below lists 73 different versions).

Outcomes

- I can use a calendar.
- I know the order of the months in the year and how many days in each one.
- I can work out on what day of the week a particular date is going to be on.

Supporting resources

Children can try more calendar activities here:
- http://www.primaryresources.co.uk/maths/mathsE2.htm

Children can read more about the *Thirty days hath September* rhyme here:
- http://www.leapzine.com/30Days.htm

Challenge Plan: Year 3

C3: locating positions on a grid; measuring and comparing weights; using units of time; sorting data using Venn and Carroll diagrams

Summary

Y3 ◯ C3.6

Logic tracks

Pairs or groups working independently

Year 3 Challenge Textbook page 67

Year 3 Challenge PCM 51

Blank cards; 1–100 number cards; shape cards

Abacus Evolve objectives

- Classify and sort data according to one or two criteria in Venn and Carroll diagrams
- Classify and describe 2D shapes, including quadrilaterals
- Recognise odd and even numbers up to at least 100

Framework objectives

- *Use Venn diagrams or Carroll diagrams to sort data and objects using more than one criterion*
- Derive and recall multiplication facts for the 2, 3, 4, 5, 6 and 10 times-tables and the corresponding division facts; recognise multiples of 2, 5 or 10 up to 1000
- Relate 2D shapes and 3D solids to drawings of them; describe, visualise, classify, draw and make the shapes
- Explain a process or present information, ensuring items are clearly sequenced, relevant details are included and accounts ended effectively

Teacher notes

Preparation
Photocopy PCM 51, one copy per child, pair or group.
Cut out some blank cards, the right size to fit in the question sections on the PCM.

Getting started
Look at Textbook page 67 with the group. Explain how a logic track can be used to sort numbers or shapes, according to questions about their properties. Make sure children understand how to use the logic track.
Put a set of number cards 1–100 and a set of 2D shape cards on the table.

Activity
Children work from Textbook page 67. They write a pair of questions about number properties on blank cards, and position them in the correct places on the blank logic track on PCM 51. (The second question will need to be written on two cards.) They then choose some number cards, and put them through the track to see which groups they end up in.
They investigate what happens when they swap the positions of the questions.
Children repeat the activity using properties of shapes, using 2D shape cards. They try out their shape logic track on others in the group.

Be aware

- Make sure children know that they should use the same question twice at the second two junctions of the logic track and that they understand why this is.

Outcomes

- I can make a logic track that sorts numbers and shapes into different groups.
- I can sort numbers by properties such as whether they are multiples of certain numbers.
- I can sort shapes by properties such as number of sides.

Supporting resources

Children can play sorting games with Venn diagrams, here:
- http://pbskids.org/cyberchase/games/logic/logic.html

Children can play sorting games with Carroll diagram games, here:
- http://www.wmnet.org.uk/wmnet/custom/files_uploaded/uploaded_resources/850/carrollv4.swf
- http://nrich.maths.org/public/viewer.php?obj_id=5729

Challenge Plan: Year 3

D3: adding using informal methods; using column addition; finding a difference by counting on; subtracting using informal methods

Summary

Y3 ◯ D3.1

Three by three squares

A small group working with an adult

Year 3 Challenge Textbook page 68

Demonstration-sized 3 × 3 grid, with cells large enough for digit cards; digit cards 0–9; paper for 3 × 3 grids

Abacus Evolve objectives

- **Y4** Add HTU + TU, HTU + HTU using informal written methods
- **Y4** Subtract HTU − TU, HTU − HTU using informal written method of complementary addition
- **Y4** Partition 2-digit numbers into T and U (revise)
- **Y4** Use known number facts and place value to add two 2-digit numbers, adding the tens first
- **Y4** Choose and use appropriate operations and appropriate ways of calculating (mental, mental with jottings, pencil and paper) to solve problems

Framework objectives

- **Y4** Refine and use efficient written methods to add and subtract 2- and 3-digit whole numbers and £.p
- **Y4** *Add or subtract mentally pairs of 2-digit whole numbers (e.g. 47 + 58, 91 − 35)*
- **Y4** Report solutions to puzzles and problems, giving explanations and reasoning orally and in writing, using diagrams and symbols
- **Y4** Respond appropriately to others in the light of alternative viewpoints

Teacher notes

Activity

- Look at Textbook page 68 together. Read the explanation of how the score of the 3 × 3 number grid should be calculated.
- Use a demonstration-sized 3 × 3 grid and ask children to place digit cards 1–9 in the cells at random. Ask half of the group to write the six horizontal 2-digit numbers and find their total. Ask the other half to do the same for the six vertical 2-digit numbers. *Are the totals the same? Can you see why not?* Ask children to add the two totals to make an overall score for the square.
- Children work from Textbook page 68. They start by working through the example 3 × 3 square on the page. They find the total of the horizontal 2-digit numbers, then the total of the vertical 2-digit numbers. They find the difference between the two totals, and then add them to find the square's score.
- Children move on to making their own 3 × 3 squares using digit cards 1–9, and finding the scores. If necessary, remind them that digits cannot be repeated.
- Next, they try to make the square with the highest possible score.
- After a few minutes, draw children together to discuss their thinking and strategies for getting larger scores. Expect some children to suggest places where the larger digits can go, e.g. put 9 in the top left corner so that it gets used as 90 twice (therefore contributing 180 to the score), or put 9 in the middle so that it gets used as 90 twice but also as 9 twice (therefore contributing 198 to the score).
- After this brief discussion, children continue trying to improve their scores. If someone thinks they have achieved the maximum score (798), ask them to explain how they can be certain this is the highest score.

Extra help

Give children a piece of blank paper with a hole cut out so that when it is placed over the grid, only two adjoining numbers can be seen. This will help children to focus on one 2-digit number at a time.

If you have time

Children continue as before but look for the minimum total possible. Is it related to the search for the maximum, but 'reversed'?

Be aware

- Make sure children understand that they are making 2-digit numbers by combining the 1-digit numbers, rather than by adding them.

Outcomes

- I can investigate different arrangements of digits in a 3 × 3 square.
- I can add 2- and 3-digit numbers together, sometimes mentally and sometimes using paper.
- I can explain my reasons for putting digits in certain places when trying to make the maximum total.

D3: adding using informal methods; using column addition; finding a difference by counting on; subtracting using informal methods

Summary

Y3 ◯ D3.2

Pentacircles and hexacircles

Individuals or pairs working independently

Year 3 Challenge Textbook page 69

Year 3 Challenge PCM 52

Abacus Evolve objectives

- Begin to use column addition to add 2- and 3-digit numbers
- Use informal written methods to record additions for 2- and 3-digit numbers

Framework objectives

- Develop and use written methods to record, support or explain addition and subtraction of 2- and 3-digit numbers
- Identify patterns and relationships involving numbers or shapes, and use these to solve problems
- Represent the information in a puzzle or problem using numbers, images or diagrams; use these to find a solution and present it in context, where appropriate using £.p notation or units of measure

Teacher notes

Preparation
Photocopy PCM 52, one or two copies per child or pair.

Getting started
Use the Textbook page to introduce the idea of a pentacircle – a large ring of five overlapping circles. Make sure children understand how the pentacircles work (five numbers are written in the 'outer circle', and five in the 'inner circle'; each circle contains three numbers), and what the rules are (the three numbers in each circle must add to 100; no number can be used more than once). Encourage children to use column addition.

Activity
Children work from Textbook page 69 and use the blank pentacircles on PCM 52 for recording. First, they complete the given pentacircle, where all the numbers are multiples of 5 and all the circles must total 100.
Children then devise their own pentacircle with circles totalling 100, using numbers other than multiples of 5.
Children move on to finding the score of a pentacircle. (The score is the total of the five numbers in the 'outer circle'.) They also find the total of the five 'inner circle' numbers.
Next, they are challenged to devise a pentacircle with the highest possible score, with individual circles still totalling 100.
Children move on to devising hexacircles, using multiples of 10, in which each circle must total 1000.

Further extension
Ask children to explore the totals of the inner numbers of the pentacircles and hexacircles, then the outer numbers. *What patterns do you see?*

Be aware

- Children will need to use a systematic approach to their explorations, in order to identify patterns.

Outcomes

- I can try out different numbers in a pentacircle until I find a combination that works.
- I can spot patterns in the numbers that work and try to explain why this might be the case.
- I can add 2- and 3-digit numbers sometimes mentally and sometimes using paper.

Supporting resources

There is a further number circle investigation here:
- http://nrich.maths.org/public/viewer.php?obj_id=961

Challenge Plan: Year 3

D3: adding using informal methods; using column addition; finding a difference by counting on; subtracting using informal methods

Summary

Y3 ◯ **D3.3**

Cryptarithm puzzles

Groups working independently

Year 3 Challenge Textbook page 70

Digit cards 0–9

Abacus Evolve objectives

- Begin to use column addition to add 2- and 3-digit numbers
- Know by heart addition and subtraction facts for pairs of numbers that total up to 20

Framework objectives

- Develop and use written methods to record, support or explain addition and subtraction of 2- and 3-digit numbers
- *Derive and recall all addition and subtraction facts for each number to 20, sums and differences of multiples of 10 and number pairs that total 100*
- Describe and explain methods, choices and solutions to puzzles and problems, orally and in writing, using pictures and diagrams
- Follow up others' points and show whether they agree or disagree in a whole-class discussion

Teacher notes

Getting started

Introduce the concept of a cryptarithm, using the first example on the Textbook page. Explain that each letter represents a digit, and that when the cryptarithm is solved, it makes a correct calculation. Encourage children to use column addition, as this will make it easier to see which digits need to be added.

Activity

Children work from Textbook page 70. They start by trying to solve three cryptarithm puzzles, using digit cards.
If possible, check on children's progress after five minutes or so. If children have got stuck on the first puzzle, give them further hints. The solution to this puzzle is 426 + 842 = 1268. For example, you could tell them that H = 4.
Children then move onto a famous cryptarithm:
SEND + MORE = MONEY.
They are then challenged to make their own simplified cryptarithms, first making arithmetically correct calculations and then substituting letters for digits, without attempting to make sensible words. They swap and try to solve each others' puzzles.
They move on to try to solve 'doubly true cryptarithms', in which the numbers make a correct calculation, and the words also express a correct addition.

Information

Cryptarithms are also called alphametics.

Be aware

- Some children may struggle to solve the puzzles, and may get frustrated. Group working will allow children to help each other, and will give them the opportunities to explain their thinking to each other.

Outcomes

- I can try to solve cryptarithm puzzles.
- I can create my own cryptarithm puzzles.
- I can add 2- and 3-digit numbers using column addition.

Supporting resources

There are more number puzzles here:
- http://www.amblesideprimary.com/ambleweb/mentalmaths/buttons.html

D3: adding using informal methods; using column addition; finding a difference by counting on; subtracting using informal methods

Summary

Y3 ◇ D3.4

Finding differences

Individuals, pairs or groups working independently

Year 3 Challenge Textbook page 71

Year 3 Challenge PCM 53

Thin card

Abacus Evolve objectives

- Find a difference between two 2- or 3-digit numbers by counting on
- Add and subtract a multiple of 10 to and from a 3-digit number, crossing 100

Framework objectives

- *Add or subtract mentally combinations of 1-digit and 2-digit numbers*
- Actively include and respond to all members of the group

Teacher notes

Preparation
Photocopy PCM 53 onto card and cut up the playing cards. If there are more than four children in the group, make two sets.

Getting started
Introduce the idea of difference, establishing that for any given number, e.g. 250, there will be two numbers that have a difference of 100 from it, i.e. 150 and 350. It may help to show this using number lines.
Show some of the cards from PCM 53 to show how they link. Explain that when they play the linking card game, children need to think about the two possible differences when they try to find the next card in the chain.

Activity
Children work from Textbook page 71. First they identify pairs of numbers that have specified differences from given numbers.
Then each child or pair takes a sub-set of six cards made from PCM 53 (the sub-sets are labelled A, B, C and D). They make a complete loop from their sub-set, and record the numbers and differences in a table. They repeat for the other three sub-sets.
Children then play a game as a group, using the cards from the PCM. One child plays a card, then play passes to their left. If the next player has a card that answers the question on the first card, they play it; if they don't, they 'pass' and play continues to move to the left. The first player with no cards left is the winner. For best results, the first card to be played should display the answer 500.

Extra help
Ask children to draw an empty number line with a mark in the middle. They choose a number betwen 75 and 125 and write it by the the mark. Ask children to find the number 50 more and 50 less than their number and write it on the number line. Then 40 more and less. Then 30, 20 and 10.

Further extension
Play the game again. Encourage children be as fast as possible, allowing a 'play when you can go' rule, instead of taking turns.

Be aware

- Children should remember that there will always be two numbers that have the same difference from a number. When playing the linking cards game they will need to choose their answer carefully, based on the answers that are available on other cards.

Outcomes

- I can find two numbers with a given difference.
- I understand that finding the difference is the same as subtracting.

Challenge Plan: Year 3

D3: adding using informal methods; using column addition; finding a difference by counting on; subtracting using informal methods

Summary

Y3 ☆ D3.5

Changing subtractions

Individuals, pairs or groups working independently

Year 3 Challenge Textbook page 72

 Number lines

Abacus Evolve objectives

- Use informal written methods to record subtractions for 2- and 3-digit numbers
- Find a difference between two 2- or 3-digit numbers by counting on
- Know what each digit in a 3-digit number represents, including 0 as a place holder
- Partition 3-digit numbers into H, T and U
- Extend use of patterns of similar calculations
- Extend understanding that subtraction is the inverse of addition

Framework objectives

- Develop and use written methods to record, support or explain addition and subtraction of 2-digit and 3-digit numbers
- *Add or subtract mentally combinations of 1-digit and 2-digit numbers*
- *Partition 3-digit numbers into multiples of 100, 10 and 1 in different ways*
- Identify patterns and relationships involving numbers or shapes, and use these to solve problems

Teacher notes

Getting started
Textbook page 72 demonstrates a method of turning difficult-looking subtractions into simpler ones, by adding or subtracting equal amounts to or from both numbers. Make sure children understand how the method works.

Activity
Children work from Textbook page 72. First they make six subtractions easier by subtracting equal amounts from both numbers, and then solve the simpler subtractions.
They then try using the same method on the next six subtractions, but this time they add equal amounts.
Children are asked to think about why adding/subtracting equal amounts to/from both numbers does not affect the difference between them. They use number lines to show why this is the case.

Extra help
Chlidren can explore adding a 1-digit number to, or subtracting it from, both numbers in some simple subtractions. This will introduce the idea that the answer does not change.

Further extension
Give children some subtractions in the context of getting change in a shop. For example, my costs £6·45. I give the shop assistant £10. How much change do I get? (10 − 6·45).
Children use what they have learned to simplify these subtractions and solve them. E.g. 10·55 − 7 = 3·55. I get £3·55 change.

Be aware

- In the Extra activity, it is possible that children will move into negative numbers. If you do not think they are ready for this, advise them to choose their numbers carefully so as to avoid this.

Outcomes

- I can turn hard subtractions into easy subtractions by adding or subtracting equal amounts.
- I understand that if I change two numbers by the same amount, the difference between them stays the same.

Challenge Plan: Year 3

D3: adding using informal methods; using column addition; finding a difference by counting on; subtracting using informal methods

Summary

Y3 D3.6 **Subtracting money amounts**

A small group working with an adult

Year 3 Challenge PCM 54

Digit cards 0–9

Abacus Evolve objectives

- **Y4** Subtract amounts of money, e.g. £8·40 − £3·76, using standard written method of decomposition
- **Y4** Use known number facts and place value to subtract one 2-digit number from another, by counting on and back
- **Y4** Subtract near multiples of 10 from 2- and 3-digit numbers
- **Y4** Choose and use appropriate operations and appropriate ways of calculating (mental, mental with jottings, pencil and paper) to solve problems

Framework objectives

- **Y4** Refine and use efficient written methods to add and subtract 2-digit and 3-digit whole numbers and £.p
- **Y4** *Add or subtract mentally pairs of 2-digit whole numbers (e.g. 47 + 58, 91 − 35)*
- **Y4** Solve one-step and two-step problems involving numbers, money or measures, including time; choose and carry out appropriate calculations, using calculator methods where appropriate
- **Y4** Respond appropriately to others in the light of alternative viewpoints

Teacher notes

Preparation
Photocopy PCM 54, one copy per child or pair. Cut out each activity.

Activity
- Explain that this lesson will involve different activities about subtracting money. Stress the approach of 'estimate first, calculate second'. Introduce and explain the different types of activity on PCM 54.
- Give children the four activities. You could either give each child or pair one activity to work on, then they move on to the next activity when they have finished, or you could allow the whole group to work on one activity at a time.
- During these subtraction activities, try to ensure that children are aware that subtraction can take different forms:
  - subtraction as matching and comparing amounts or measures (e.g. *How much more does this one cost?*)
  - subtraction as moving forward or back along a number line
  - subtraction as the giving and taking of an amount, which decreases the giver's amount and increases the taker's (e.g. *Ben gives £10 to Jo, so Ben has £10 less than before, but Jo has £10 more*)
  - subtraction within the breaking of an amount into two parts which can then be put together (e.g. splitting £1).
- In all cases, children need to become more aware that they can solve any subtraction by 'adding on to the smaller number to make the larger number'.

If you have time
Give different children a specific money amount (e.g. £5·46) for which they must devise a subtraction with that amount as the answer (e.g. £9·21 − £3·75). Children swap subtractions and see if they can get the right answer.

Be aware

- Children may find it challenging to use subtraction in real-life contexts. If so, it will be helpful for them to use number lines to support their thinking.

Outcomes

- I can count on from a smaller number to a larger number.
- I can subtract amounts of money by counting on.

Supporting resources

The 'Change game' and 'Bargain hunt' activities involve adding and subtracting money:
- http://www.bbc.co.uk/skillswise/numbers/measuring/money/game.shtml

Challenge Plan: Year 3

E3: understanding division as grouping; multiplying by 10 and 100; recognising simple equivalent fractions; finding totals and giving change

Summary

Y3 ⬡ E3.1

Multiplication arithmagons

Individuals or pairs working independently

Year 3 Challenge Textbook page 73

Year 3 Challenge PCM 55

Calculators (optional)

Abacus Evolve objectives

- Understand division as grouping
- Rehearse division as the inverse of multiplication
- Extend understanding that multiplication can be done in any order

Framework objectives

- Use practical and informal written methods to support multiplication and division of 2-digit numbers (e.g. 13 × 3, 30 ÷ 4); round remainders up or down, depending on the context
- Understand that division is the inverse of multiplication and vice versa; use this to derive and record related multiplication and division number sentences
- Describe and explain methods, choices and solutions to puzzles and problems, orally and in writing, using pictures and diagrams
- Follow up others' points and show whether they agree or disagree in a whole-class discussion

Teacher notes

Preparation
Photocopy PCM 55, several copies per child or pair.

Getting started
Show children the multiplication arithmagons on Textbook page 73 and check that they understand how they work. If necessary, quickly go through question 1 as a group.

Activity
Children work from Textbook page 73, recording their work on PCM 55. First, they try to solve triangular arithmagons for which three out of the six numbers are given.
Then they explore how many different solutions are possible when only two products are given.
They make up their own examples of triangular arithmagons with only two products given, and share these with their group.
Children move on to explore possible solutions to arithmagons where one product is given as well as the number in the circle opposite.
Again, they make up their own examples and share.
Finally, children investigate arithmagons of other shapes – square, pentagon and hexagon.

If you have time
Children can use calculators to make arithmagons with larger products. They share these with the group for others to solve.

Be aware

- Some arithmagons will yield multiplications that are beyond children's knowledge of times-tables. If children choose to explore these larger numbers, encourage them to use known number facts to find the answer, before resorting to a calculator.

Outcomes

- I can investigate and find different solutions to arithmagon puzzles.
- I remember the 2, 3, 4, 5, 6 and 10 times-tables.
- I understand that division is the opposite of multiplication.

Supporting resources

Children can try these addition arithmagon puzzles:
- http://nrich.maths.org/public/viewer.php?obj_id=2670
- http://nrich.maths.org/public/viewer.php?obj_id=5573

Challenge Plan: Year 3

E3: understanding division as grouping; multiplying by 10 and 100;
recognising simple equivalent fractions; finding totals and giving change

Summary

Y3 ⬡ E3.2

Multiplication grids 2

A small group working with an adult

2 cm² paper; calculators (optional)

Abacus Evolve objectives

- **Y4** Know by heart the multiplication facts for the 2, 3, 4, 5 and 10 times-tables
- **Y4** Derive division facts corresponding to the 2, 3, 4, 5 and 10 times-tables
- **Y4** Know the multiplication facts for the 6 times-table, and the corresponding division facts
- **Y4** Begin to know the multiplication facts for the 8 times-table, and the corresponding division facts
- **Y4** Begin to know the multiplication facts for the 9 times-table, and the corresponding division facts
- **Y4** Begin to know the multiplication facts for the 7 times-table, and the corresponding division facts
- **Y4** Use doubling or halving to find new facts from known facts

Framework objectives

- **Y4** *Derive and recall multiplication facts up to 10 × 10, the corresponding division facts and multiples of numbers to 10 up to the tenth multiple*
- **Y4** Identify the doubles of 2-digit numbers; use to calculate doubles of multiples of 10 and 100 and derive the corresponding halves
- **Y4** Report solutions to puzzles and problems, giving explanations and reasoning orally and in writing, using diagrams and symbols
- **Y4** Respond appropriately to others in the light of alternative viewpoints

Teacher notes

Preparation
Make empty 2 × 2, 3 × 3 and 4 × 4 square grids on 2 cm² paper, for multiplying numbers.

Activity
- Show a blank 2 × 2 multiplication grid. *Where can four numbers be placed so that the missing numbers can be found?* (They can be the factors around the edge, or a mix of factors and products.) Depending on the position of the starting numbers, different solutions are possible. Illustrate this using numbers with lots of factors, e.g. 24, 30, 36 and 48. Children should conclude that any four spaces can be left blank.
- Children create 3 × 3 multiplication grids. Encourage them to use challenging multiplication tables, e.g. 6, 7, 8, 9, 11, 12, 14, 15, 16 and 18. They should use facts they already know to work out the higher times-tables, e.g. ×15 is ×10 plus ×5; and ×14 is ×7 doubled.
- Children work in pairs to decide how to change completed squares into puzzles, working out how many numbers they need to show so that the puzzle can be solved. They swap puzzles with others in the group and try to solve each other's. Encourage them to look for patterns in where the revealed numbers can be placed. (At least one piece of information must be given for each column and row.)

- Challenge them to solve this puzzle, where only six of the 15 numbers are given:

×	5		
2			30
	15		
4		40	

- Extend to 4 × 4 grids, and if appropriate to larger numbers using calculators.

Be aware

- When asking children to work with multiplications that are beyond their current knowledge of times-tables, encourage them to use known number facts to find the answer, rather than resorting to a calculator.

Outcomes

- I can look for and find patterns in multiplication grids.
- I can recall times-tables and use them to help me create and solve multiplication puzzles.

Supporting resources

Children can practise multiplication here:
- http://www.bbc.co.uk/skillswise/numbers/wholenumbers/multiplication/timestables/flash3.shtml

E3: understanding division as grouping; multiplying by 10 and 100; recognising simple equivalent fractions; finding totals and giving change

Summary

Y3 ◇ E3.3

Multiplying and dividing by 10, 100 and 1000

Individuals, pairs or groups working independently

Year 3 Challenge Textbook page 74

Year 3 Challenge PCM 56

Thin card

Abacus Evolve objectives

- **Y4** Begin to multiply integers by 100
- **Y4** Multiply or divide any integer up to 1000 by 10 and understand the effect
- **Y4** Use decimal notation for tenths

Framework objectives

- **Y4** Multiply and divide numbers to 1000 by 10 and then 100 (whole number answers), understanding the effect; relate to scaling up or down
- **Y4** Use decimal notation for tenths and hundredths and partition decimals; relate the notation to money and measurement; position 1- and 2-place decimals on a number line
- **Y4** Take different roles in groups and use the language appropriate to them, including roles of leader, reporter, scribe and mentor

Teacher notes

Preparation
Photocopy PCM 56 onto card and cut out the playing cards. If more than four children will be playing, make two sets.

Activity
Children work from Textbook page 74. First, they solve some multiplication questions involving multiplying by 10, 100 and 1000. Next, they work out which card is missing from an incomplete set of linking cards.
Then each child or pair takes a sub-set of six cards made from PCM 56 (the sub-sets are labelled A, B, C and D). They make a complete chain, so that the question on each card is answered on the next card.
Children repeat for the other three sub-sets.
Children then play a game as a group, using all 24 cards. They shuffle and deal them out. One child plays a card with 70 on it, then play passes to their left. If the next player has a card that answers the question on the first card, they play it; if they don't, they 'pass' and play continues to move to the left. The first player with no cards left is the winner.

Extra help
Children can practise multiplying and dividing 2-digit numbers by 10 first.

Further extension
Children can explore multiplying and dividing amounts of money by 10, and discuss what they notice.

Be aware

- Some children may have difficulty with the multiplications and divisions that include decimals. If needed, use a place-value grid to demonstrate what happens when a 1-digit number is divided by 10.

Outcomes

- I can multiply and divide numbers by 10, 100 and 1000.
- I understand that dividing is the opposite of multiplying

E3: understanding division as grouping; multiplying by 10 and 100; recognising simple equivalent fractions; finding totals and giving change

Summary

Y3 ◯ E3.4

Repeated halving

A small group working with an adult

Year 3 Challenge Textbook page 75

Rulers and other objects with straight edges; pairs of scissors; large squares of sugar paper (different colours)

Abacus Evolve objectives

- **Y4** Find fractions of numbers, quantities and shapes
- **Y4** Find quarters by halving halves
- **Y4** Describe and visualise 2D shapes
- **Y4** Rehearse the names of common 2D shapes
- **Y4** Recognise equilateral and isosceles triangles

Framework objectives

- **Y4** Find fractions of numbers, quantities or shapes (e.g. $\frac{1}{5}$ of 30 plums, $\frac{3}{8}$ of a 6 by 4 rectangle)
- **Y4** Draw polygons and classify them by identifying their properties, including their line symmetry
- **Y4** Identify and use patterns, relationships and properties of numbers or shapes; investigate a statement involving numbers and test it with examples
- **Y4** Respond appropriately to others in the light of alternative viewpoints

Teacher notes

Activity

- Textbook page 75 introduces the idea of repeatedly halving a square to find fractions of it. Discuss the different ways of halving and see if children can explain why the third and fourth shapes are halves.
- Split the group into two smaller groups. Give each small group a large sugar paper square (if possible, give each group a different coloured square). Ask each group to fold their square in half diagonally, as shown in the first example on the Textbook page, and then cut along the line. *What shape are the two halves?* Ask the groups to swap one triangle with each other, so they each have one of each colour.
- *Try to halve one of the triangles.* Encourage children to see that they can fold the triangle in half and cut along the fold. Ask the groups to swap one of their new triangles.
- Ask the groups to continue. Every time they make a smaller triangle, they cut one in half and give half to the other group. *What do you notice about the shape of each piece?* Children continue until they cannot halve the shapes any more.

$\frac{1}{2}$, $\frac{1}{4}$, $\frac{1}{16}$, $\frac{1}{8}$, $\frac{1}{32}$, $\frac{1}{64}$

- Ask one group to spread out their set of shapes on a surface. Ask children to work as one large group to try to arrange the shapes in a square.
- Ask them to look at each of the pieces and work out what fraction of the original square each piece is. They label each piece with its fraction.
- Children answer questions 1 to 6 on the Textbook page.
- Move on to repeatedly halving a square using the fourth method shown on the Textbook page. This time, children do not cut their shape but draw it. They begin by drawing a very large square and then repeatedly find mid-points of the sides and join these, each time creating a smaller square.

Extra help

Give each child two copies of a quadrilateral, a different quadrilateral for each child. Children explore joining their two shapes together and seeing what outlines they can create. Remind them that the two side that are joined must be the same length. This will introduce the ideas of halving and doubling shapes.

Be aware

- Children who understand the activity may still need support with accurate folding and cutting, to identify fractions of the square that are exactly the same size.

Outcomes

- I can see what happens when we halve a shape again and again.
- I can recognise and describe different 2D shapes.

Challenge Plan: Year 3

E3: understanding division as grouping; multiplying by 10 and 100; recognising simple equivalent fractions; finding totals and giving change

Summary

Y3 ◇ E3.5

Matching fractions, matching money

Individuals, pairs or groups working independently

Year 3 Challenge Textbook page 76

Year 3 Challenge PCM 57

Thin card

Abacus Evolve objectives

- Begin to recognise simple equivalent fractions
- Compare familiar fractions
- Use informal written methods to record additions for 2- and 3-digit numbers
- Rehearse £.p notation
- Find totals, give change and work out which coins to pay

Framework objectives

- Read and write proper fractions (e.g. $\frac{3}{7}$, $\frac{9}{10}$) interpreting the denominator as the parts of a whole and the numerator as the number of parts; identify and estimate fractions of shapes; use diagrams to compare fractions and establish equivalents
- Develop and use written methods to record, support or explain addition and subtraction of 2-digit and 3-digit numbers
- Solve one-step and two-step problems involving numbers, money or measures, including time, choosing and carrying out appropriate calculations

Teacher notes

Preparation
Photocopy PCM 57 onto card, one copy per child or pair. Cut out both sets of cards.

Activity
Children work from Textbook page 76. They identify fractions from a given set that are equal to, more than and less than a half. They move on to finding fractions that are equivalent to a quarter and to another fraction of their choice.
Children use the fractions cards from PCM 57. They find the eight pairs of equivalent fractions, record them, and then think of a third equivalent fraction for each pair.
Children then use the money cards from PCM 57. They find pairs of amounts that add to make the target amounts shown on the Textbook page. Each pair consists of one amount less than £1 and one amount more than £1.

If you have time
Children use the money cards and arrange them in pairs of their choice to give new totals. They write down the target totals and exchange them with a partner who tries to find the right pairs.

Be aware

- At first children may not understand how fractions that look different can represent the same amount. Use arrays or fraction walls to demonstrate this. Highlight the relationship between equivalent fractions (the numerator and the denominator have both been multiplied by the same number.)

Outcomes

- I can recognise fractions that are the same.
- I can add and subtract pounds and pence.

Supporting resources

Children can practise matching fractions with this game:
- http://pbskids.org/cyberchase/games/equivalentfractions/index.html

Challenge Plan: Year 3

E3: understanding division as grouping; multiplying by 10 and 100; recognising simple equivalent fractions; finding totals and giving change

Summary

Y3 ⚬ E3.6

Coins – old and new

Pairs or groups working independently

Year 3 Challenge Textbook page 77

Pre-decimal coins (optional); internet (optional)

Abacus Evolve objectives

- Use informal written methods to record additions for 2- and 3-digit numbers
- Use informal written methods to record subtractions for 2- and 3-digit numbers
- Rehearse £.p notation
- Find totals, give change and work out which coins to pay
- Solve 'real-life' problems involving money (comparing amounts)

Framework objectives

- Develop and use written methods to record, support or explain addition and subtraction of 2- and 3-digit numbers
- Solve one- and two-step problems involving numbers, money or measures, including time, choosing and carrying out appropriate calculations
- Develop and use specific vocabulary in different contexts

Teacher notes

Getting started
Look at Textbook page 77 with the group and discuss the introduction of decimal currency in 1971. Look at the pictures of the old coins, and the relationships between different amounts.

Activity
Children work from Textbook page 77. They learn about the relationships between different coins in the pre-decimal system. They find totals of sets of old coins, and then work out how much change they would get from 1 pound after paying given amounts of money.

Extra help
Children may find it useful to see some real pre-decimal coins.

Further extension
Children can use the internet to find the cost of some toys in the pre-decimal era (e.g. 1970). They can express these prices in modern money

If you have time
Children can use the internet to find out about other non-decimal currencies.

Be aware

- Some children may struggle to keep the old system of currency clear in their heads and distinct from the current system. By working in pairs or groups, children should be able to clarify their thoughts by talking them through.

Outcomes

- I know some of the coins that were used before 1971.
- I can find the total of a set of old coins.
- I can work out what change I would get after paying with old coins.

Supporting resources

Look here for more information about pre-decimal British currency:
- http://www.wwwk.co.uk/culture/old-money/index.htm
- http://www.retrowow.co.uk/retro_britain/old_money/old_money.html

Year 3 Autumn Assessment Activity

Shape totals

Assessment Foci: L3/4 Using and applying mathematics (Problem solving; Communicating; Reasoning); L3 Number (Numbers and the number system; Solving numerical problems)

Resources: PCMs A–D; A3 paper (optional)

Lesson 1 – preparation – 1 hour

Part 1 – introduction – 20 minutes

Hand out PCMs A–C. Ask children to each choose a 1-digit number less than 10, and write it in each corner of the first triangle on PCM A. *Write the total of the corner numbers in the centre of the triangle.*

Ask children to do the same for the first square on PCM B and the first pentagon on PCM C. Establish through discussion that for triangles, squares and pentagons the centre number is, respectively, 3×, 4× and 5× the chosen corner number.

Ask children to look at the triangles again. *Can you make a triangle with a total of 20, but with a different number in each corner?* They may not use 0; at this stage you may also want to ask them not to use 1. (If 1 is used, the number of possible solutions is greatly increased.)

Part 2 – development – 25 minutes

Cut up copies of PCMs A–C so that there is a good supply of each shape on separate pieces of paper. Ask children to create shapes with totals less than 1000. They then use these to create puzzles for other children in the group, by copying out the shapes but missing out one number. Ask children to swap puzzles. When a child has solved a puzzle, they check the solution with its creator.

Part 3 – plenary – 15 minutes

Can you make a triangle where all the corner numbers are different, and the total is 6? They should quickly find the solution: 1, 2, 3. *What different corner numbers could we use to make a total of 7? What about a total of 8? 9? 10?* Extension: challenge children to solve similar problems using squares (totals greater than 9) and pentagons (totals greater than 14).

Lesson 2 – investigation – 1 hour

Part 1 – introduction – 10 minutes

Begin the lesson by looking at squares and pentagons with low totals: either share the examples children devised in the preparation lesson, or explore the possibilities now as a group.

You are now going to investigate patterns and find out how many different arrangements of numbers with the same total you can find.

Write 12 in the centre of a triangle. Ask children to write three different (positive) whole numbers in its corners. They may not use 0. *How many different solutions are there? Can you see a pattern? How many different solutions do you think you could make with a total of 12? What about pentagons?*

Give each child clean copies of PCMs A–C.

Part 2 – investigation – 30 minutes

Ask each child to investigate a different total (start with 25, 26, 27 and 28; if there are more than four children, 23, 24 and 29 can also be used). Ask children not to use 1 or 2 (to reduce the number of possible solutions).

Ask children to record some brief initial ideas and conjectures about the investigation. Encourage them to plan how they will record their work.

Children work individually to find as many different possible combinations of numbers that give their total, looking at all three shapes. Encourage them to look for patterns and try to work out why they occur.

Part 3 – conclusions – 20 minutes

Children write a final report of their investigation. This could take the form of an A3 poster, showing their initial thoughts, their journey and findings along the way, and any conclusions or fresh ideas.

Ask children to complete the self-assessment sheet on PCM D.

If time allows, children can view each other's posters and compare the patterns they have found.

Shape totals

Objectives

These are the objectives that could be met by children doing this Assessment Activity.

Strand	Abacus Evolve objectives	Framework objectives
Using and applying mathematics	**Y3** Extend use of patterns of similar calculations **Y3** Recognise odd and even numbers up to at least 50	**Y3** Represent the information in a puzzle or problem using numbers, images or diagrams; use these to find a solution and present it in context, where appropriate using £.p notation or units of measure **Y3** Follow a line of enquiry by deciding what information is important; make and use lists, tables and graphs to organise and interpret the information **Y3** Identify patterns and relationships involving numbers or shapes, and use these to solve problems **Y3** Describe and explain methods, choices and solutions to puzzles and problems, orally and in writing, using pictures and diagrams
Knowing and using number facts	**Y3** Know by heart addition and subtraction facts for pairs of numbers that total up to 20 **Y4** Use knowledge of sums or differences of odd/even numbers to check calculations	*Y3 Derive and recall all addition and subtraction facts for each number to 20, sums and differences of multiples of 10 and number pairs that total 100* **Y4** Use knowledge of rounding, number operations and inverses to estimate and check calculations
Calculating	**Y3** Continue to recognise that addition can be done in any order **Y3** Add several numbers by finding pairs that total 9, 10 or 11	*Y3 Add or subtract mentally combinations of 1- and 2-digit numbers*

Shape totals

Answers

Note: these answers are not exhaustive.

Preparation

Part 1 – introduction
The following combinations of three numbers produce a total of 20.

1, 2, 17	2, 3, 15	3, 4, 13	4, 5, 11	5, 6, 9
1, 3, 16	2, 4, 14	3, 5, 12	4, 6, 10	5, 7, 8
1, 4, 15	2, 5, 13	3, 6, 11	4, 7, 9	
1, 5, 14	2, 6, 12	3, 7, 10		
1, 6, 13	2, 7, 11	3, 8, 9		
1, 7, 12	2, 8, 10			
1, 8, 11				
1, 9, 10				

Part 3 – plenary
Triangles

$6 = 1 + 2 + 3$
$7 = 1 + 2 + 4$
$8 = 1 + 2 + 5 = 1 + 3 + 4$
$9 = 1 + 2 + 6 = 1 + 3 + 5$
$10 = 1 + 2 + 7 = 1 + 3 + 6 = 1 + 4 + 5$

Squares

$10 = 1 + 2 + 3 + 4$
$11 = 1 + 2 + 3 + 5$
$12 = 1 + 2 + 3 + 6 = 1 + 2 + 4 + 5$
$13 = 1 + 2 + 3 + 7 = 1 + 2 + 4 + 6 = 1 + 3 + 4 + 5$
$14 = 1 + 2 + 3 + 8 = 1 + 2 + 4 + 7 = 1 + 2 + 5 + 6 = 1 + 3 + 4 + 6$

Pentagons

$15 = 1 + 2 + 3 + 4 + 5$
$16 = 1 + 2 + 3 + 4 + 6$
$17 = 1 + 2 + 3 + 4 + 7 = 1 + 2 + 3 + 5 + 6$
$18 = 1 + 2 + 3 + 4 + 8 = 1 + 2 + 3 + 5 + 7$
$19 = 1 + 2 + 3 + 4 + 9 = 1 + 2 + 3 + 5 + 8 = 1 + 2 + 3 + 6 + 7$
$ = 1 + 3 + 4 + 5 + 6$

Investigation

Part 1 – introduction
The following combinations of numbers produce a total of 12:
Triangles: 1, 2, 9 1, 3, 8 1, 4, 7 1, 5, 6 2, 3, 7 2, 4, 6 3, 4, 5
Squares: 1, 2, 3, 6 1, 2, 4, 5
Pentagons: no solutions

Part 2 – investigation – 30 minutes
The following combinations produce a total of 25.

Triangles		Squares	Pentagons
3, 4, 18	5, 6, 14	3, 4, 5, 13	3, 4, 5, 6, 7
3, 5, 17	5, 7, 13	3, 4, 6, 12	
3, 6, 16	5, 8, 12	3, 4, 7, 11	
3, 7, 15	5, 9, 11	3, 4, 8, 10	
3, 8, 14	6, 7, 12	3, 5, 6, 11	
3, 9, 13	6, 8, 11	3, 5, 7, 10	
3, 10, 12	6, 9, 10	3, 5, 8, 9	
4, 5, 16	7, 8, 10	3, 6, 7, 9	
4, 6, 15		4, 5, 6, 10	
4, 7, 14		4, 5, 7, 9	
4, 8, 13			
4, 9, 12			
4, 10, 11			

Total	Triangles	Squares	Pentagons
25	21	10	1
26	24	15	1
27	27	18	2
28	30	23	2

Some children may choose to continue beyond pentagons to hexagons or heptagons. Note that there is only a solution for a heptagon if the total is 28 or more. The sole solution for 28 is 1, 2, 3, 4, 5, 6, 7.

Year 3 Spring Assessment Activity

Diamond totals

Assessment Foci: L3/4 Using and applying mathematics (Problem solving; Communicating; Reasoning); L3 Number (Numbers and the number system; Mental methods)

Resources: PCMs D–G; coloured pencils

Lesson 1 – preparation – 1 hour

Part 1 – introduction – 15 minutes

Give children PCM E. Ask children to colour the three diamonds that can be found in a 2 by 2 triangle.

Draw a large 2 by 2 triangle on the board. Fill in the numbers 5, 10, 15 and 20 in any order. *What are the totals for each diamond? If we rearrange the four numbers, what other totals can we make? How many different sets of totals are possible?*

Give children two copies of PCM F to record their working. The bottom section of PCM E gives them three examples to get them started.

Part 2 – development – 30 minutes

Give children clean copies of PCM F. Ask each child to choose a times table, and choose four consecutive facts. For example, a child might choose the 3 times table, and choose 9, 12, 15 and 18. They explore the different ways to arrange their four numbers in 2 by 2 triangles, and find the possible diamond totals. They record their arrangements on PCM F.

Children can then turn their triangles into puzzles for each other to solve: *Write your name and the three totals for one of your triangles on a piece of paper. Give the totals to someone else. Don't tell them what numbers are in the triangle!* Children solve each other's triangles by deducing the numbers involved.

Part 3 – plenary – 15 minutes

Write any four numbers between 1 and 10 in a triangle. What do the numbers in each diamond multiply to give? What multiplication table do all the products belong to?

Children invent some multiplication puzzles. Ask them to pool the puzzles, and take some away to solve before lesson 2.

Lesson 2 – investigation – 1 hour

Part 1 – introduction – 10 minutes

Give children PCM G. *How many diamonds can you find in a 3 by 3 triangle? The diamonds point in three different directions. Colour one type of diamond in each of these three triangles. Use a different colour for each diamond.*

Draw a large 3 by 3 triangle on the board. Fill in the digits 1 to 9 in any order. Ask children for the three totals, and the grand total, for each type of diamond in turn. *What is the total of all nine diamonds?* Discuss the following questions as a group:

- *Is it possible to rearrange the nine numbers in the triangle so that the three direction totals are the same?*
- *How could we make the overall total bigger? Smaller? What arrangement has the maximum overall total? minimum?*

Part 2 – investigation – 35 minutes

Ask children to record some brief initial ideas and conjectures about the investigation. Encourage them to plan how they will record their work.

Children work individually to make different arrangements of the digits 1 to 9 in the blank triangles on PCM G, aiming to answer the two questions above.

Extension: ask children to multiply the numbers in the diamonds, rather than adding them.

Part 3 – conclusions – 15 minutes

Children write a final report of their investigation, showing their journey and findings along the way, with any conclusions or fresh ideas.

Ask children to complete the self-assessment sheet on PCM D.

Diamond totals

Objectives

These are the objectives that could be met by children doing this Assessment Activity.

Strand	Abacus Evolve objectives	Framework objectives
Using and applying mathematics	**Y3** Extend use of patterns of similar calculations	**Y3** Represent the information in a puzzle or problem using numbers, images or diagrams; use these to find a solution and present it in context, where appropriate using £.p notation or units of measure **Y3** Follow a line of enquiry by deciding what information is important; make and use lists, tables and graphs to organise and interpret the information **Y3** Identify patterns and relationships involving numbers or shapes, and use these to solve problems **Y3** Describe and explain methods, choices and solutions to puzzles and problems, orally and in writing, using pictures and diagrams
Knowing and using number facts	**Y3** Know by heart addition and subtraction facts for pairs of numbers that total up to 20 **Y3** Know by heart the multiplication facts for the 5 and 10 times tables **Y3** Know by heart the multiplication facts for the 3 times table **Y3** Know by heart the multiplication facts for the 4 times table **Y3** Begin to know multiplication facts for the 6 times table and corresponding division facts	**Y3** *Derive and recall all addition and subtraction facts for each number to 20, sums and differences of multiples of 10 and number pairs that total 100* **Y3** Derive and recall multiplication facts for the 2, 3, 4, 5, 6 and 10 times tables and the corresponding division facts; recognise multiples of 2, 5 or 10 up to 1000
Calculating	**Y3** Continue to recognise that addition can be done in any order **Y3** Add several numbers by finding pairs that total 9, 10 or 11 **Y3** Add and subtract two 2-digit numbers, beginning to cross a multiple of 10	**Y3** *Add or subtract mentally combinations of 1- and 2-digit numbers*

Diamond totals

Answers

Note: these answers are not exhaustive.

Preparation

Part 1 – introduction

These are the three diamonds in the 2 by 2 triangle:

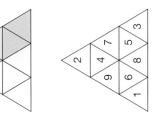

There are 24 possible arrangements for four numbers. However, there are only four different sets of totals. The totals change when the centre number changes.

Centre number	Totals
5	15, 20, 25
10	15, 25, 30
15	20, 25, 35
20	25, 30, 35

Part 3 – plenary

When multiplying, all the products will be in the multiplication table of the central number in the triangle, because all three diamonds include this number. For example:

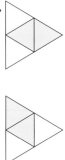
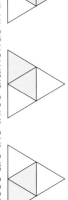

Products: 40, 48, 56

Investigation

Part 1

This diagram shows three diamonds all pointing in the same direction (slanting down from the left). There are also three that slant down from the right, and three that lie vertically from the base (nine in all).

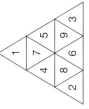

Totals from left: 14 + 11 + 8 = 33
Totals from right: 13 + 13 + 7 = 33
Totals from base: 15 + 12 + 6 = 33

Part 2 – investigation

It is possible to arrange the numbers so that the three direction totals are the same. For example:

Three numbers are included in three diamonds each; three numbers are included in two diamonds each; and three numbers appear in only one diamond each. Larger totals occur when larger numbers are counted more often. The maximum overall total is 108 and the minimum is 72 (12 × 9 and 8 × 9 respectively).

Maximum

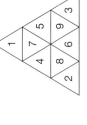

Totals from left: 14 + 12 + 12 = 38
Totals from right: 11 + 10 + 15 = 36
Totals from base: 12 + 8 + 14 = 34
Overall total = 108

Minimum

Totals from left: 7 + 10 + 7 = 24
Totals from right: 8 + 10 + 8 = 26
Totals from base: 6 + 10 + 6 = 22
Overall total = 72

Year 3 Summer Assessment Activity

Homes for gnomes

Assessment Foci: L3/4 Using and applying mathematics (Problem solving; Communicating; Reasoning); L3/4 Shape space and measures (Properties of shape; Properties of position and movement)

Resources: PCMs D and H–J; linking cubes; 2 cm squared paper (optional)

Lesson 1 – preparation – 1 hour

Part 1 – introduction – 20 minutes

Give children PCM H and some linking cubes. *A tribe of gnomes have asked you to make a set of designs for some new houses they want to build. You are going to use cubes to represent the designs. Each cube is a room.* Children make a house each out of five cubes, with at least one room upstairs. You may wish to provide squared paper so that children can draw 3 by 3 plots for their homes.

Ask children to share their house designs. Explain that the 3D models must be viewed from three directions (front, side, and top/plan/bird's eye view) to produce a design that can be faxed to the gnome builder. Go through the example on PCM H and make sure children understand how the three views relate to the 3D arrangement.

Part 2 – development – 25 minutes

Give children several copies of PCM I. Ask them to make as many different houses as they can using five cubes, and record the three views for each on the PCM.

Part 3 – plenary – 15 minutes

Bring the group together. *We cannot send the gnomes any designs which are repeats of the same building.* Children look at all their designs, eliminating any that match each other (matches include any design that is the mirror image of another, the rotation of another, or another design upside down). Ask children to work as a team to agree a set of unique designs ready to fax to the gnome builder.

Lesson 2 – investigation – 1 hour

Part 1 – introduction – 10 minutes

The gnomes were delighted with your designs! They have recommended you to another tribe of gnomes who want you to design some homes for them.

Explain that this time, children can use six cubes to build each house, on 4 by 3 plots. Houses should not be more than three storeys high, including any roof – linking prisms can be used to make sloping roofs. Linking prisms can be used in addition to the six cubes. Again, you may wish children to draw some plots on squared paper before they begin.

Children must also follow one of the sets of rules from PCM J (or make up their own set). Discuss these with the group before they begin making their models. Note that one of the rules states that the building should not be symmetrical, but that this does not mean that none of the views can be symmetrical. *How many different designs do you think you can make that follow the rules?*

Part 2 – investigation – 30 minutes

Ask children to record some brief initial ideas and conjectures about the investigation. Encourage them to plan how they will record their work.

Children work individually to create their designs and draw the plans. Before the plans are finalised, children check that they work by asking another member of the group to make the houses from the plans.

Part 3 – conclusions – 20 minutes

Children write a final report of their investigation, showing their journey and findings along the way, with any conclusions or fresh ideas. Each design should be accompanied by some 'unique selling points' (e.g. *This house has a garage port under an overhanging room / front and back gardens / a flat roof space for development*).

Ask children to complete the self-assessment sheet on PCM D.

Year 3 Summer Assessment Activity

Homes for gnomes

Objectives

These are the objectives that could be met by children doing this Assessment Activity.

Strand	Abacus Evolve objectives	Framework objectives
Using and applying mathematics		**Y3** Represent the information in a puzzle or problem using numbers, images or diagrams; use these to find a solution and present it in context, where appropriate using £.p notation or units of measure **Y3** Identify patterns and relationships involving numbers or shapes, and use these to solve problems **Y3** Describe and explain methods, choices and solutions to puzzles and problems, orally and in writing, using pictures and diagrams
Understanding shape	**Y3** Classify and describe common 3D shapes by properties: number of faces, edges, vertices; types of face **Y3** Identify and sketch lines of symmetry in simple shapes **Y3** Recognise shapes with no lines of symmetry **Y4** Describe and visualise 3D shapes **Y4** Visualise 3D shapes from 2D drawings and identify simple nets of solid shapes	**Y3** Relate 2D shapes and 3D solids to drawings of them; describe, visualise, classify, draw and make the shapes **Y3** Draw and complete shapes with reflective symmetry and draw the reflection of a shape in a mirror line along one side **Y4** Visualise 3D objects from 2D drawings and make nets of common solids

Homes for gnomes

Answers

Investigation

The following example follows the second set of rules.

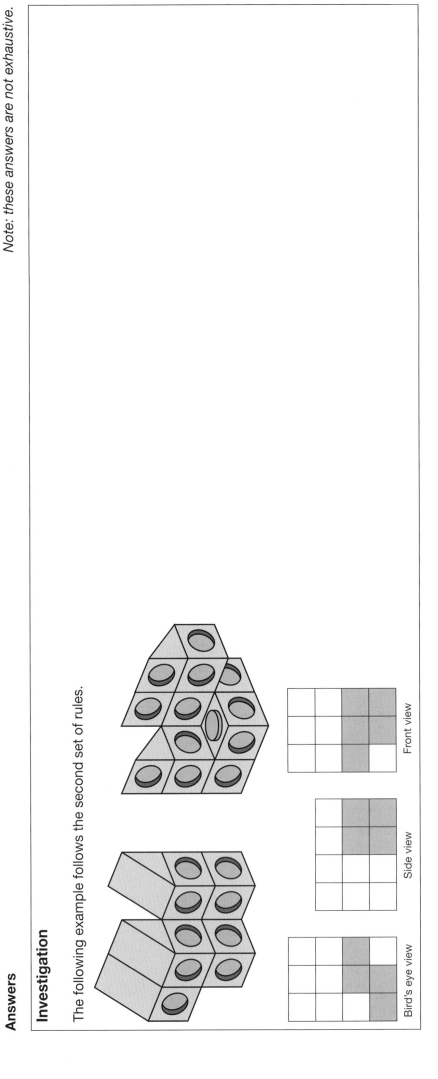

Bird's eye view   Side view   Front view

PCM Contents

Growing on trees I

1

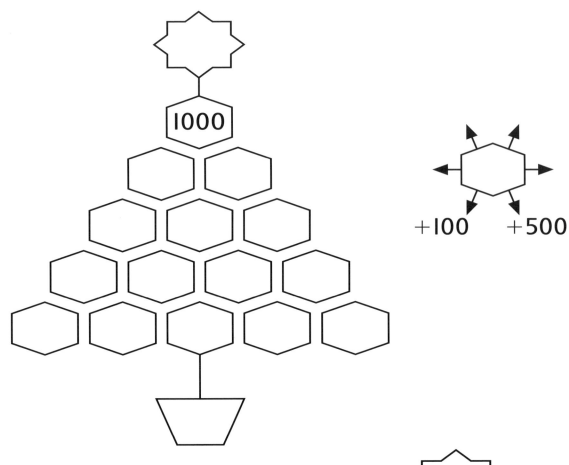

2

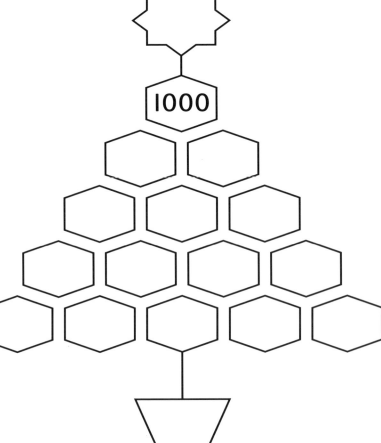

Growing on trees 2

3

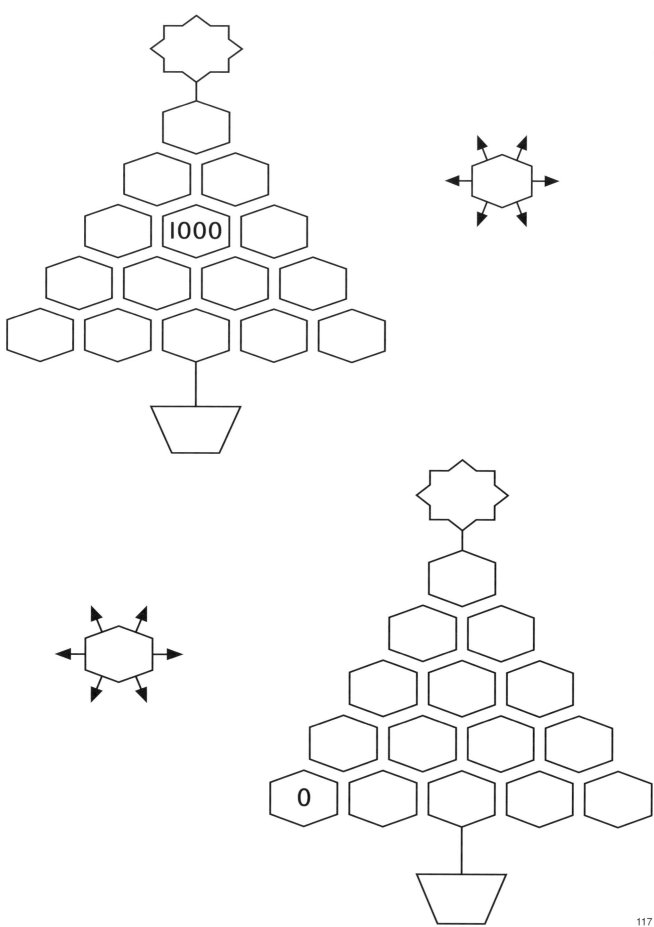

Abacus Evolve Year 3 Challenge PCM © Pearson Education Ltd 2009

Making moves I

I to 100 square

1	2	3	4	5	6	7	8	9	10
11	12	13	14	15	16	17	18	19	20
21	22	23	24	25	26	27	28	29	30
31	32	33	34	35	36	37	38	39	40
41	42	43	44	45	46	47	48	49	50
51	52	53	54	55	56	57	58	59	60
61	62	63	64	65	66	67	68	69	70
71	72	73	74	75	76	77	78	79	80
81	82	83	84	85	86	87	88	89	90
91	92	93	94	95	96	97	98	99	100

101 to 200 square

101	102	103	104	105	106	107	108	109	110
111	112	113	114	115	116	117	118	119	120
121	122	123	124	125	126	127	128	129	130
131	132	133	134	135	136	137	138	139	140
141	142	143	144	145	146	147	148	149	150
151	152	153	154	155	156	157	158	159	160
161	162	163	164	165	166	167	168	169	170
171	172	173	174	175	176	177	178	179	180
181	182	183	184	185	186	187	188	189	190
191	192	193	194	195	196	197	198	199	200

Making moves 2

5 to 500 square

5	10	15	20	25	30	35	40	45	50
55	60	65	70	75	80	85	90	95	100
105	110	115	120	125	130	135	140	145	150
155	160	165	170	175	180	185	190	195	200
205	210	215	220	225	230	235	240	245	250
255	260	265	270	275	280	285	290	295	300
305	310	315	320	325	330	335	340	345	350
355	360	365	370	375	380	385	390	395	400
405	410	415	420	425	430	435	440	445	450
455	460	465	470	475	480	485	490	495	500

110 to 900 square

110	120	130	140	150	160	170	180
190	200	210	220	230	240	250	260
270	280	290	300	310	320	330	340
350	360	370	380	390	400	410	420
430	440	450	460	470	480	490	500
510	520	530	540	550	560	570	580
590	600	610	620	630	640	650	660
670	680	690	700	710	720	730	740
750	760	770	780	790	800	810	820
830	840	850	860	870	880	890	900

Abacus Evolve Year 3 Challenge PCM © Pearson Education Ltd 2009

Make a number

1

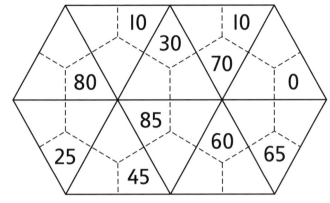

2

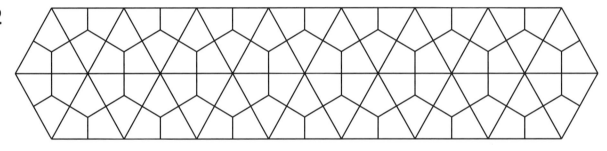

3

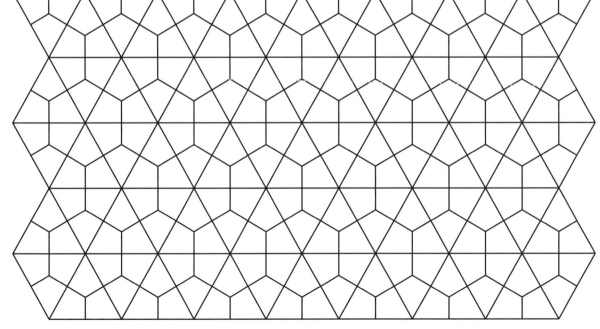

Circular counting stick

Abacus Evolve Year 3 Challenge PCM © Pearson Education Ltd 2009

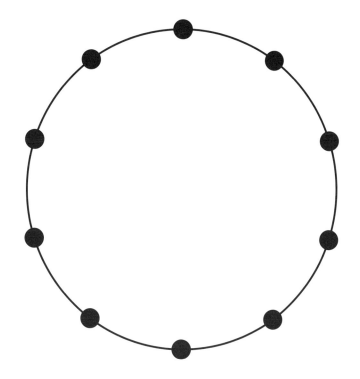

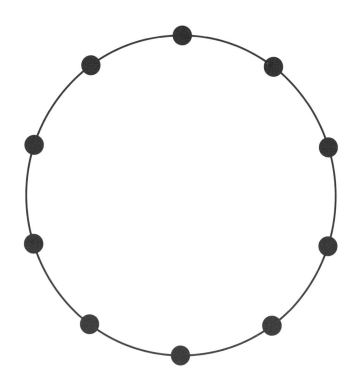

Rows of houses

1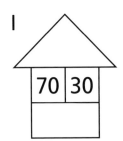

2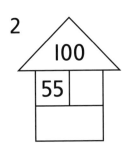

3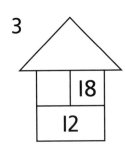

4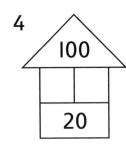

5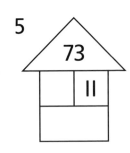

6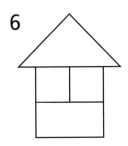

7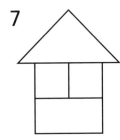

8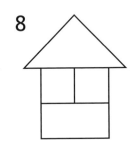

9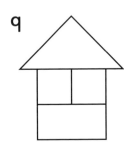

10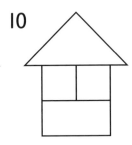

11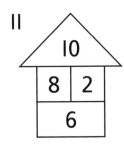

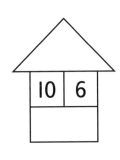

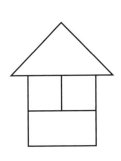

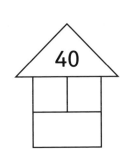

12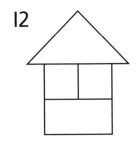

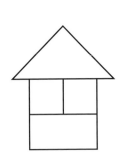

Magic squares I

Abacus Evolve Year 3 Challenge PCM © Pearson Education Ltd 2009

Magic squares 2

1	8	6
9	4	2
5	3	7

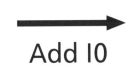

Add 10

11		
		17

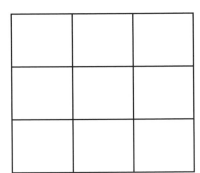

Tile patterns

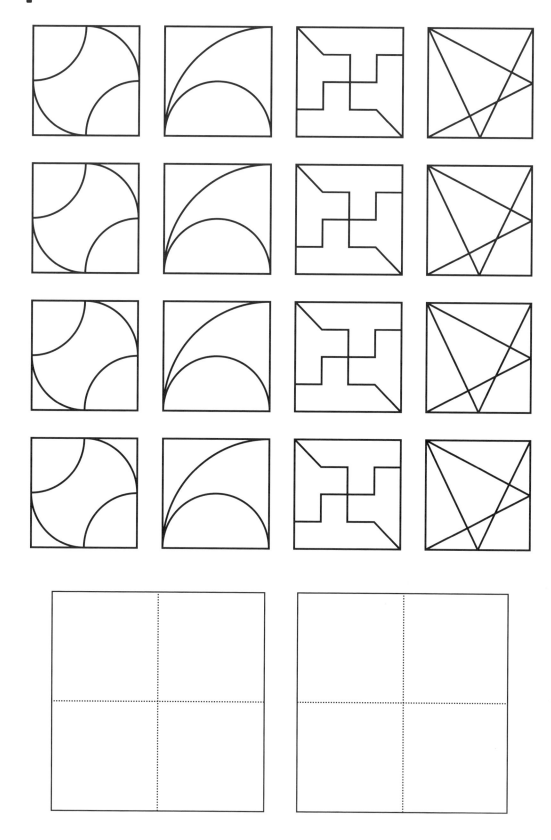

Abacus Evolve Year 3 Challenge PCM © Pearson Education Ltd 2009

Estimating measurements

What you are measuring:					
Name	Between		Difference	In/out	Winner
The actual measure is:					

What you are measuring:					
Name	Between		Difference	In/out	Winner
The actual measure is:					

Making journeys

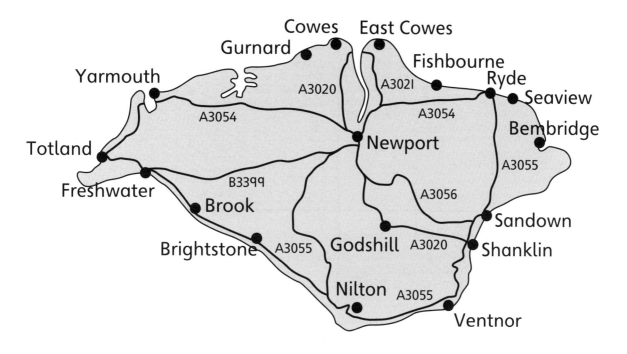

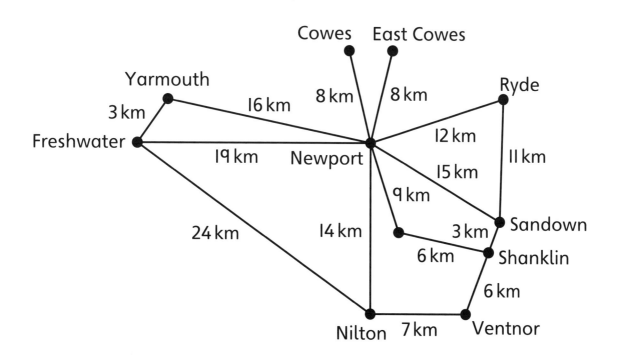

Main road map for Isle of Wight

Abacus Evolve Year 3 Challenge PCM © Pearson Education Ltd 2009

Minibeasts

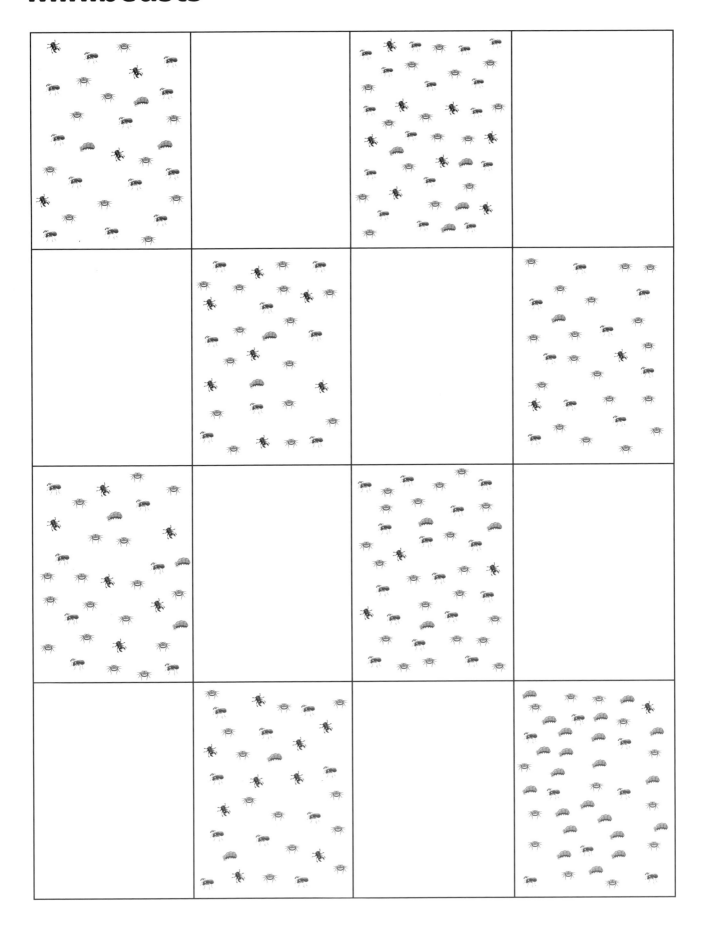

Abacus Evolve Year 3 Challenge PCM © Pearson Education Ltd 2009

Boxed number games

4	5	9	2
9	2	3	6
1	8	7	4
6	5	1	8

5	9	234	2
231	5	2	12
8	6	7	229
6	230	7	7

9	13	474	4
473	5	8	14
7	15	2	476
11	467	16	6

6	103	884	7
887	4	5	104
102	7	8	883
5	886	103	6

Subtraction cross-number puzzles

Cross-number puzzle I

A		B		C	D
		E			
F				G	
H			I		

Clues across		Clues down	
A		A	
C		B	
E		D	
F		G	
G			
H			
I			

Cross-number puzzle 2

	A		B		C
D			E	F	
G		H			
I				J	
		K			

Clues across		Clues down	
A		A	
D		B	
E		C	
G		D	
I		F	
J		H	
K			

130

How much time?

Abacus Evolve Year 3 Challenge PCM © Pearson Education Ltd 2009

80 A How many seconds in 2 minutes?	80 B How many minutes in 1 hour 40 min?	80 C How many seconds in 3 minutes?	80 D How many minutes in 1 hour 10 min?
120 A How many seconds in 1 min 30 s?	100 B How many minutes in 1 hour 15 min?	180 C How many seconds in 2 minutes?	70 D How many minutes in 3 hours?
90 A How many seconds in 1 min 10 s?	75 B How many minutes in 1 hour 10 min?	120 C How many seconds in 1 min 25 s?	180 D How many minutes in 1 hour 50 min?
70 A How many seconds in 1 min 40 s?	70 B How many minutes in 1 hour 45 min?	85 C How many seconds in 1 min 15 s?	110 D How many minutes in 1 hour 45 min?
100 A How many seconds in 1 min 50 min?	105 B How many minutes in 3 hours?	75 C How many seconds in 1 min 45 s?	105 D How many minutes in 1 hour 30 min?
110 A How many seconds in 1 min 20 s?	180 B How many minutes in 1 hour 20 min?	105 C How many seconds in 1 min 20 s?	90 D How many minutes in 1 hour 20 min?

Matching times

Start times

11:45	11:55	12:15	12:25	12:35

Numbers of minutes

23 min	18 min	13 min	33 min	28 min

For each new time, find the matching start time and number of minutes.
Say whether the new time is earlier or later.

Start time	Number of minutes	New time
		12:08
		11:37
12:15	13 minutes earlier	12:02
		12:58
		1:03
		11:27
		12:08
		12:48
		11:57
		12:58

Linking multiplication and division

24 A divide by 8	**24** B divide by 6	**24** C divide by 3	**24** D divide by 4
3 A multiply by 5	**4** B multiply by 5	**8** C multiply by 4	**6** D multiply by 2
15 A divide by 3	**20** B divide by 4	**32** C divide by 8	**12** D divide by 3
5 A multiply by 4	**5** B multiply by 3	**4** C multiply by 3	**4** D multiply by 8
20 A divide by 5	**15** B divide by 5	**12** C divide by 2	**32** D divide by 4
4 A multiply by 6	**3** B multiply by 8	**6** C multiply by 4	**8** D multiply by 3

Abacus Evolve Year 3 Challenge PCM © Pearson Education Ltd 2009

Function machines

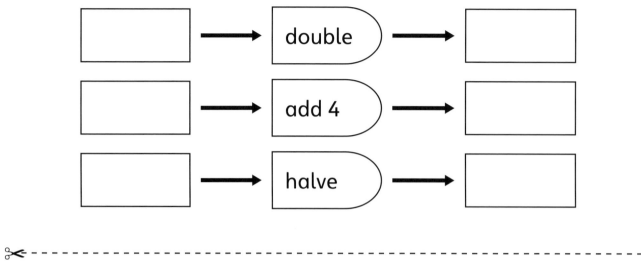

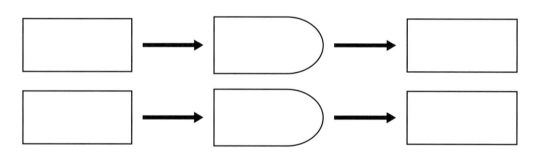

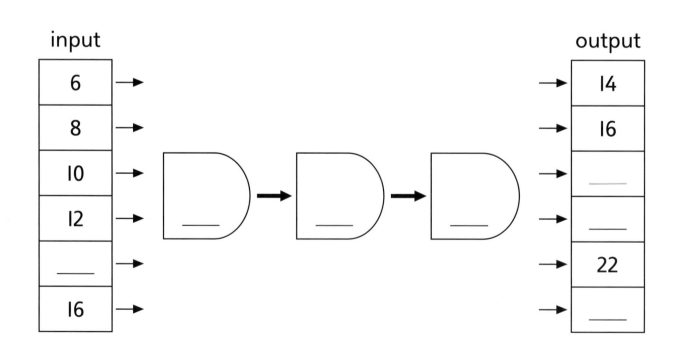

Doubling and halving shapes

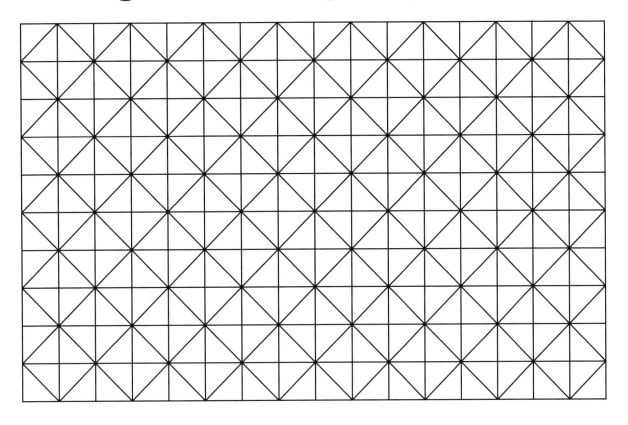

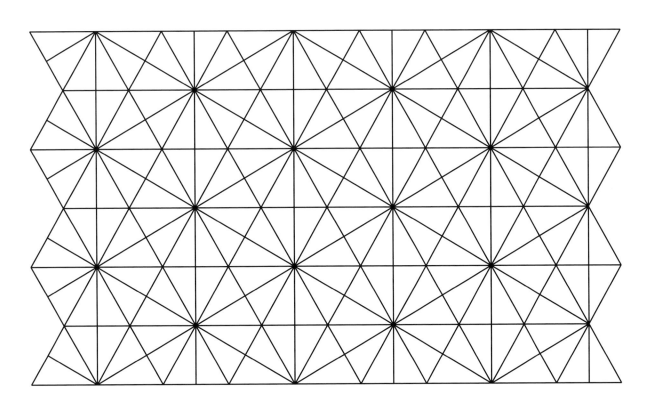

Abacus Evolve Year 3 Challenge PCM © Pearson Education Ltd 2009

Ordering numbers

100 A The largest number from 144, 142, 1044	**100** B The largest number from 256, 240, 252	**100** C The largest number from 321, 300, 319	**100** D A number between 9190 and 9120
1044 A A number between 230 and 290	**256** B The smallest number from 225, 239, 227	**321** C Exactly half-way between 280 and 232	**9130** D Exactly half-way between 350 and 292
256 A The smallest number from 342, 321, 330	**225** B The smallest number from 105, 110, 103	**256** C A number between 2003 and 2504	**321** D The smallest number from 146, 144, 151
321 A Exactly half-way between 1091 and 1015	**103** B A number between 3301 and 3339	**2225** C Exactly half-way between 135 and 153	**144** D Exactly half-way between 6210 and 6240
1053 A The largest number from 199, 218, 225	**3321** B A number between 1354 and 1501	**144** C The largest number from 103, 99, 102	**6225** D The smallest number from 264, 270, 256
225 A A number between 90 and 105	**1447** B The largest number from 87, 100, 97	**103** C Exactly half-way between 93 and 107	**256** D The smallest number from 100, 123, 102

Abacus Evolve Year 3 Challenge PCM © Pearson Education Ltd 2009

Counting on and back

37	39	56	61
62	72	77	106
109	134	201	216
272	317	422	487
522	699	711	737

W	W	W	W	W
£11·54	£15·99	£21·49	£27·99	£31·99
X	X	X	X	X
£24·28	£25·33	£33·78	£38·83	£40·33
Y	Y	Y	Y	Y
£49·35	£50·00	£54·40	£54·85	£59·95
Z	Z	Z	Z	Z
£18·74	£24·69	£29·24	£30·19	£39·69

Olympic rings

Complements linking cards

Abacus Evolve Year 3 Challenge PCM © Pearson Education Ltd 2009

24 A From 560, make 1000.	**24** B From £2·80 how many pence to make £10?	**24** C From 400p, how many pounds to make £10?	**24** D From £2, how many 10p pieces to make £10?
440 A From 70p, how many pence to make £1?	**720** B From 40, make 100.	**6** C From £5·60, how many pence to make £10?	**80** D From £7, how many 50p pieces to make £10?
30 A From 20, make 100.	**60** B From £9·20, how many pence to make £10?	**440** C From £7, how many 10p pieces to make £10?	**6** D From 150, make 1000.
80 A From 20, make 1000.	**80** B From 65p, how many pence to make £1?	**30** C From £4, how many 10p pieces to make £10?	**850** D From 65, make 100.
980 A From £1·50, how many pence to make £10?	**35** B From 40p, how many 10p pieces to make £1?	**60** C From £6·50, how many 10p pieces to make £10?	**35** D From 70, make 100.
850 A From 76, make 100.	**6** B From 76p, how many pence to make £1?	**35** C From 760, how many tens to make 1000?	**30** D From £9·76, how many pence to make £10?

Prisms and anti-prisms

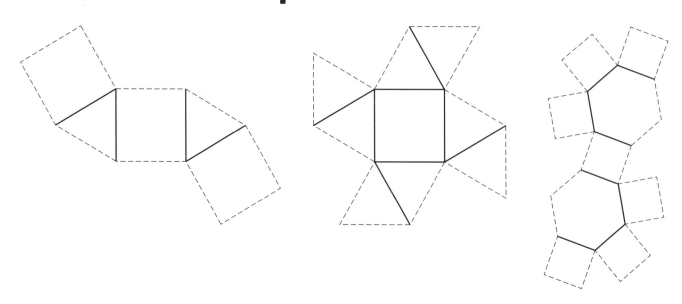

Prisms

Base polygon	Vertices	Edges	Faces
Equilateral triangle	6	9	5
Square			
Regular pentagon			
Regular hexagon			

Anti-prisms

Base polygon	Vertices	Edges	Faces
Equilateral triangle	6	12	8
Square			
Regular pentagon			
Regular hexagon			

Abacus Evolve Year 3 Challenge PCM © Pearson Education Ltd 2009

Record times

Olympic records for the modern triathlon

Men	I hour, 48 minutes, 24 seconds
Women	I hour, 58 minutes, 28 seconds

World records for the marathon

Men	2 hours, 3 minutes, 59 seconds
Women	2 hours, 15 minutes, 25 seconds

World and Olympic records for the 100 metre sprint

Men	9·69 seconds
Women	10·49 seconds

World records for the 400 metre sprint

Men	43·18 seconds
Women	47·60 seconds

FI British Grand Prix: fastest laps

In 2008	I hour, 39 minutes, 9 seconds
In 2009	I hour, 21 minutes, 43 seconds

Round the World Clipper race

Started	16 September 2007
Finished	6 July 2008

Frequency tables

In February, a team of birdwatchers recorded the species of birds they saw in a 1 km square grid reference.

The table shows how many birdwatchers recorded seeing each species of bird.

Species of bird	Number of reports
Mallard	20
Cormorant	3
Grey heron	5
Sparrowhawk	16
Kestrel	7
Moorhen	20
Coot	20
Oystercatcher	14
Black-headed gull	20
Common gull	20
Herring gull	18
Feral pigeon	20
Woodpigeon	10
Collared dove	20
Green woodpecker	1
Grey wagtail	12
Pied wagtail	14
Wren	6

Species of bird	Number of reports
Dunnock	1
Robin	17
Blackbird	20
Song thrush	6
Blackcap	2
Goldcrest	5
Long-tailed tit	2
Coal tit	3
Blue tit	16
Great tit	8
Magpie	20
Jackdaw	13
Carrion crow	20
Starling	20
House sparrow	15
Chaffinch	16
Greenfinch	5
Goldfinch	3

Box-and-whisker plots

In a race, 'the field' means all the runners.

The field of the women's 10 000 metres race

Place	Time	Place	Time
1	29 min 54 s	13	31 min 14 s
2	29 min 56 s	14	31 min 22 s
3	30 min 22 s	15	31 min 30 s
4	30 min 26 s	16	31 min 31 s
5	30 min 36 s	17	31 min 32 s
6	30 min 37 s	18	31 min 40 s
7	30 min 39 s	19	31 min 46 s
8	30 min 40 s	20	32 min
9	30 min 51 s	21	32 min 20 s
10	30 min 55 s	22	32 min 21 s
11	31 min 1 s	23	32 min 24 s
12	31 min 12 s		

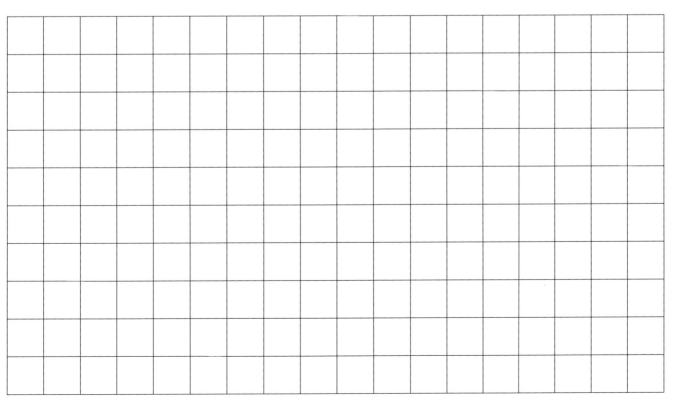

Abacus Evolve Year 3 Challenge PCM © Pearson Education Ltd 2009

Star names and real names

Star name	Letters	Real name	Letters
Angelina Jolie	13	Angelina Jolie Voight	19
Axl Rose		William Bailey	
Busta Rhymes		Trevor Smith	
David Walliams		David Williams	
Demi Moore		Demetria Guynes	
Elle MacPherson		Eleanor Gow	
Elton John		Reginald Dwight	
Eminem		Marshal Mathers	
Freddie Mercury		Farrokh Bulsara	
Harry Hill		Matthew Hall	
Hulk Hogan		Terry Bollea	
Ja Rule		Jeffrey Atkins	
Jennifer Aniston		Jennifer Anastassakis	
Jimi Hendrix		Johnny Hendrix	
Madonna		Madonna Ciccone	
Mel Gibson		Columcille Gibson	
Michael Caine		Maurice Micklewhite	
Natalie Portman		Natalie Hershlag	
Nicolas Cage		Nicolas Coppola	
Ozzy Osbourne		John Osbourne	
Pink		Alecia Moore	
Queen Latifah		Dana Owens	
Snoop Dogg		Calvin Broadus	
Sting		Gordon Sumner	
The Rock		Dwayne Johnson	
Tiger Woods		Eldrick Woods	
Tom Cruise		Thomas Mapother	
Vin Diesel		Mark Vincent	

Higher number squares

701–800 square

701	702	703	704	705	706	707	708	709	710
711	712	713	714	715	716	717	718	719	720
721	722	723	724	725	726	727	728	729	730
731	732	733	734	735	736	737	738	739	740
741	742	743	744	745	746	747	748	749	750
751	752	753	754	755	756	757	758	759	760
761	762	763	764	765	766	767	768	769	770
771	772	773	774	775	776	777	778	779	780
781	782	783	784	785	786	787	788	789	790
791	792	793	794	795	796	797	798	799	800

1201–1300 square

1201	1202	1203	1204	1205	1206	1207	1208	1209	1210
1211	1212	1213	1214	1215	1216	1217	1218	1219	1220
1221	1222	1223	1224	1225	1226	1227	1228	1229	1230
1231	1232	1233	1234	1235	1236	1237	1238	1239	1240
1241	1242	1243	1244	1245	1246	1247	1248	1249	1250
1251	1252	1253	1254	1255	1256	1257	1258	1259	1260
1261	1262	1263	1264	1265	1266	1267	1268	1269	1270
1271	1272	1273	1274	1275	1276	1277	1278	1279	1280
1281	1282	1283	1284	1285	1286	1287	1288	1289	1290
1291	1292	1293	1294	1295	1296	1297	1298	1299	1300

Money grid

£ 10	£ 20	£ 30	£ 40	£ 50	£ 60	£ 70	£ 80	£ 90	£ 100
£ 110	£ 120	£ 130	£ 140	£ 150	£ 160	£ 170	£ 180	£ 190	£ 200
£ 210	£ 220	£ 230	£ 240	£ 250	£ 260	£ 270	£ 280	£ 290	£ 300

Abacus Evolve Year 3 Challenge PCM © Pearson Education Ltd 2009

Squares to zero

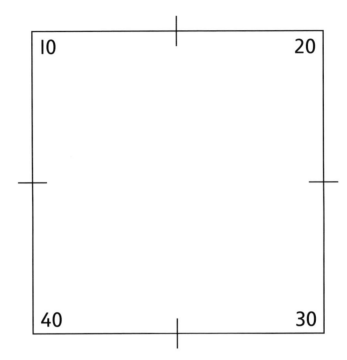

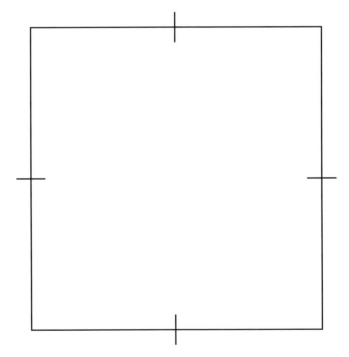

Addition walls

Abacus Evolve Year 3 Challenge PCM © Pearson Education Ltd 2009

1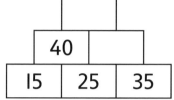

2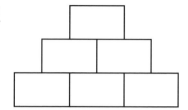

4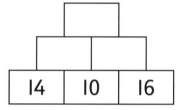

5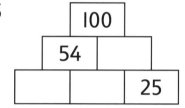

6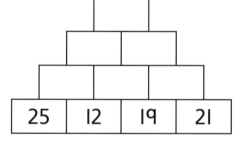

7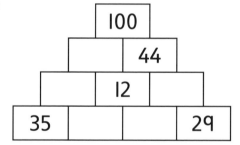

8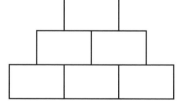

9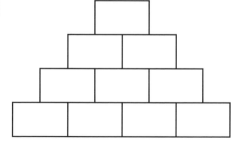

Hundreds and thousands linking cards

1500 A + 300	**1500** B + 1200	**1500** C − 600	**1500** D + 600
1800 A + 700	**2700** B − 1800	**900** C double it	**2100** D − 1300
2500 A − 400	**900** B + 1200	**1800** C − 600	**800** D double it
2100 A + 600	**2100** B − 500	**1200** C + 2400	**1600** D + 2000
2700 A − 1500	**1600** B halve it	**3600** C − 2000	**3600** D − 1100
1200 A + 300	**800** B + 700	**1600** C − 100	**2500** D − 1000

Magic numbers

Abacus Evolve Year 3 Challenge PCM © Pearson Education Ltd 2009

1
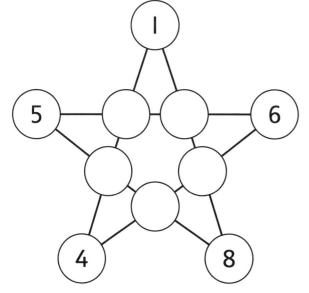

3
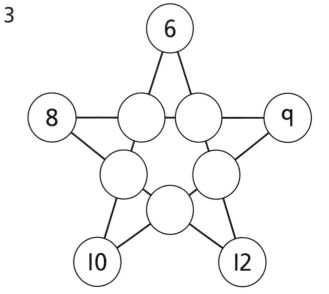

4
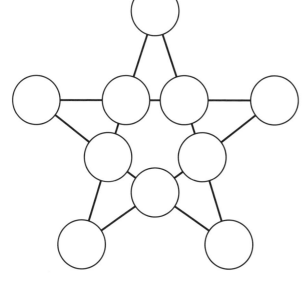

5
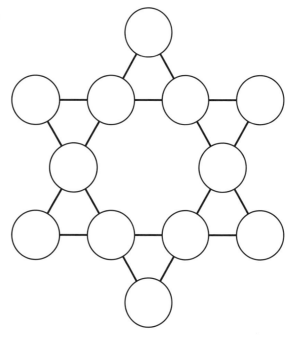

Digital roots

Numbers

Number	Number +99	Number −99
1		
2		
3		

Digital roots

Number	Number +99	Number −99	Number +98	Number −98
4				
5				
6				

Abacus Evolve Year 3 Challenge PCM © Pearson Education Ltd 2009

Multiplication linking cards

60 A Divide by 6	60 B Divide by 5	60 C Divide by 4	60 D Divide by 10
10 A Multiply by 3	12 B Multiply by 6	15 C Multiply by 6	6 D Multiply by 9
30 A Divide by 5	72 B Divide by 2	90 C Divide by 9	54 D Divide by 6
6 A Multiply by 12	36 B Divide by 6	10 C Multiply by 4	9 D Multiply by 10
72 A Divide by 6	6 B multiply by 5	40 C Divide by 2	90 D Divide by 6
12 A Multiply by 5	30 B Multiply by 2	20 C Multiply by 3	15 D Multiply by 4

Ants and elephants

Ant 1–5 mm long	Blue whale 30 m long	DNA width 2 nm	Giant millipede 30–40 cm long
Human 1–2 m high	Bacteria (large) 600 microns	Ostrich 2·5–3·0 m high	Red blood cell 8–9 microns
Amino acid 0·8 nm long	Bee hummingbird 4–6 cm long	Bacteria (small) 100 nm long	Giant clam 1·0–1·2 m wide
Cold virus 20 nm long	Pollen grain 15–25 microns	Koala 70–80 cm long	Elephant 3–4 m high

1000 nanometres (nm) = 1 micrometre (micron)
1000 microns = 1 mm   1000 mm = 1 m

Range	Living thing
0.1–0.9 nm	
1–9 nm	
10–99 nm	
100–999 nm	
1–9 micron	
10–99 microns	
0.1–0.9 mm	
1–9 mm	ant
1–9 cm	
10–99 cm	
1–9 m	elephant
10–99 m	blue whale

Escape from 100:1

Rule A

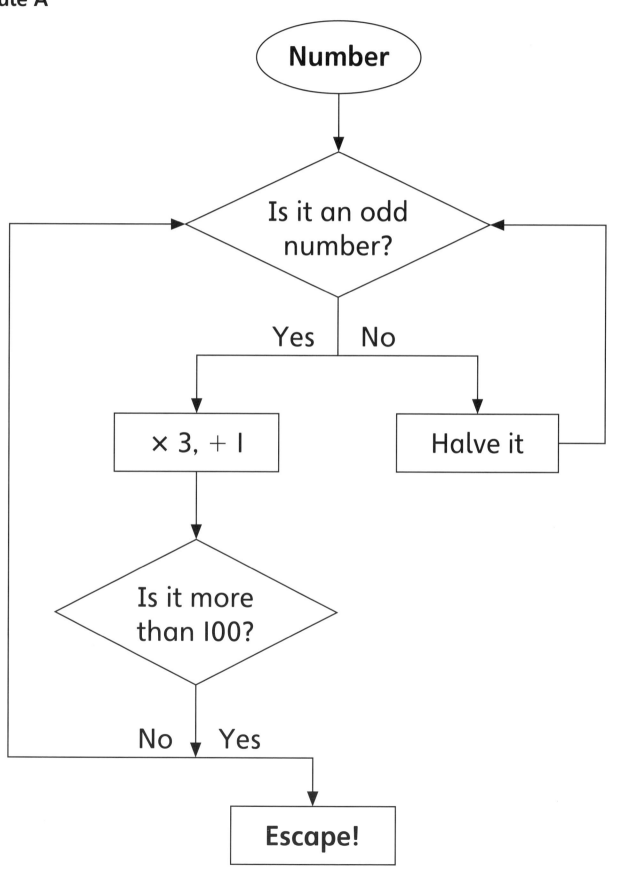

Abacus Evolve Year 3 Challenge PCM © Pearson Education Ltd 2009

Escape from 100: 2

Rule B

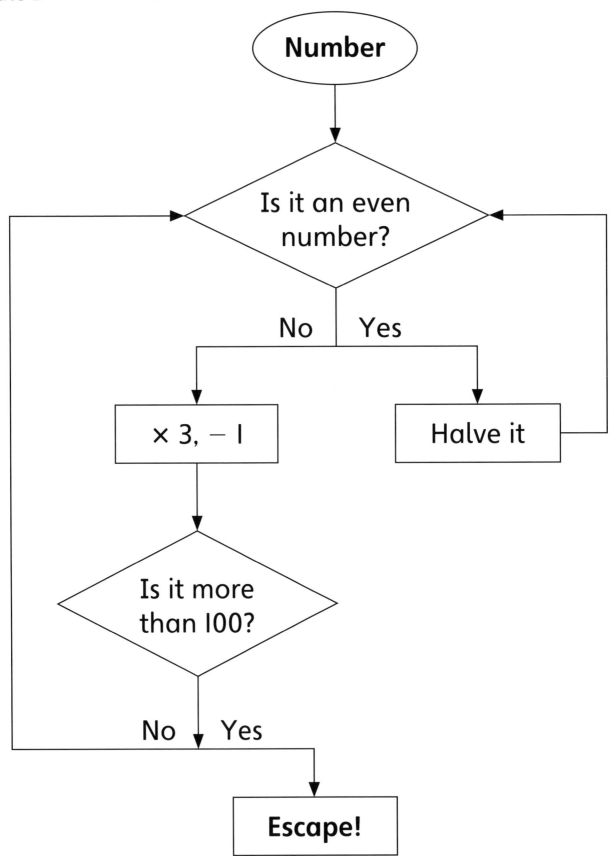

Rounding up and down

Abacus Evolve Year 3 Challenge PCM © Pearson Education Ltd 2009

Rounding and estimating

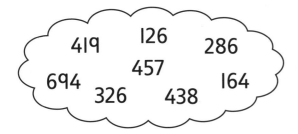

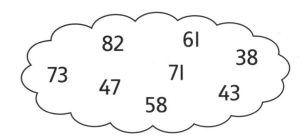

To play

- Take turns to be the Game Master.
- The Game Master chooses one number from each cloud and decides whether to add or find the difference.
- Players estimate the lower and upper numbers which the exact answer will fall between, and write their estimates on the sheet.
- The Game Master works out the exact answer, using a calculator if they need. How close are everyone's estimates?
- Only use the last two columns if you are playing for points.

Calculation:			Exact answer:	
Players' names	Lower	Upper	Difference	Winner

Calculation:			Exact answer:	
Players' names	Lower	Upper	Difference	Winner

Abacus Evolve Year 3 Challenge PCM © Pearson Education Ltd 2009

Doubling, doubling and doubling

	×2	×4	×8	
1	2	4	8	
2	4			
3				
4				
5				
6				
7				
8				
9				
10				
11				
12				
13				
14				
15				

20 × 4	23 × 4	25 × 4	29 × 4	36 × 4
20 × 8	23 × 8	25 × 8	29 × 8	36 × 8

84	196	140	22	37
24	32	216	328	264
35	41	21	96	49
296	176	128	33	27

Multiplication and division cross-number puzzles

Cross-number puzzle 1

	A		B		C
D			E	F	
G				H	
I		J		K	
		L			

Cross-number puzzle 2

A		B		C	D
		E			
F				G	
H			I		

Cross-number puzzle 3

	A		B		C
D			E		
		F			
G				H	
		I			

Clues for puzzle 3

Across	Down
A	A
D	B
E	C
F	D
G	F
H	H
I	

Centres of enlargement

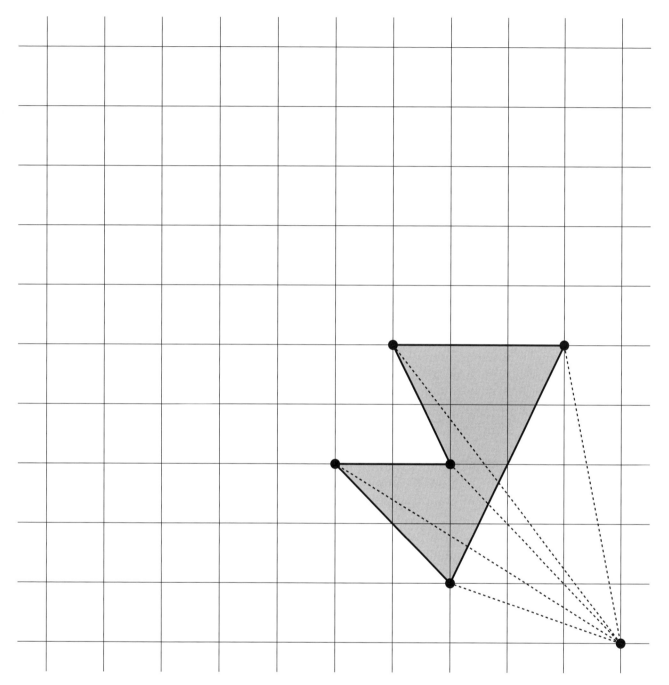

Abacus *Evolve* Year 3 Challenge PCM © Pearson Education Ltd 2009

Routes around shapes

Mathematical worms

3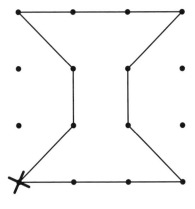

4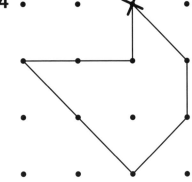

5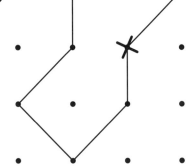

1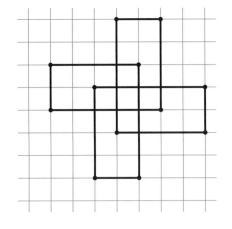

2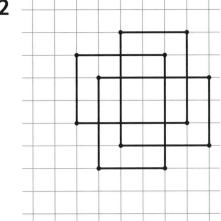

3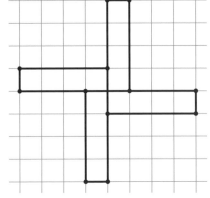

British cities map

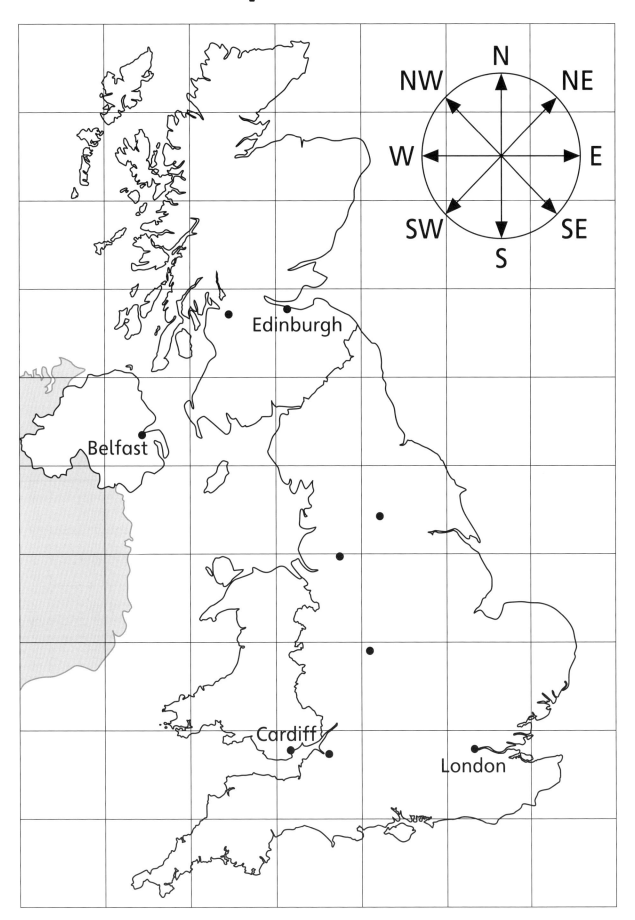

Abacus Evolve Year 3 Challenge PCM © Pearson Education Ltd 2009

British cities table

Cities in Britain with the largest populations (2001 Census)

Rank	City	Country	Code	Population
1	LONDON	England		7 172 091
2	Birmingham	England		970 892
3	Leeds	England		715 404
4	Glasgow	Scotland		577 869
5	Sheffield	England		513 234
6	Bradford	England		467 665
7	EDINBURGH	Scotland		448 624
8	Liverpool	England		439 477
9	Manchester	England		392 819
10	Bristol	England		380 615
11	CARDIFF	Wales		305 353
12	Coventry	England		300 848
13	Leicester	England		279 921
14	BELFAST	N Ireland		276 459
15	Nottingham	England		266 988

Map of Jersey I

1 Write the letter and number codes on the grid.

2 Then write the grid references of the outline. Start at A10 and go clockwise around the map.

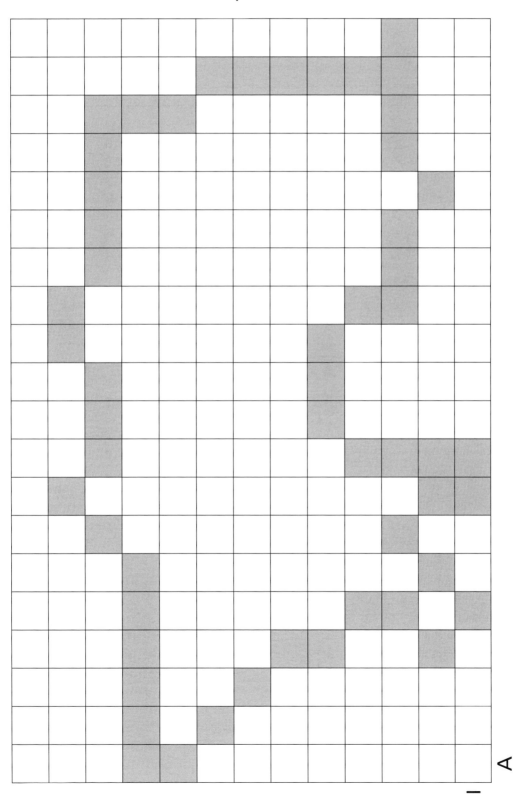

Abacus Evolve Year 3 Challenge PCM © Pearson Education Ltd 2009

Map of Jersey 2

3 Write the coordinates of:
- St John's Village
- St Helier
- St Brelade
- St Peter's Village

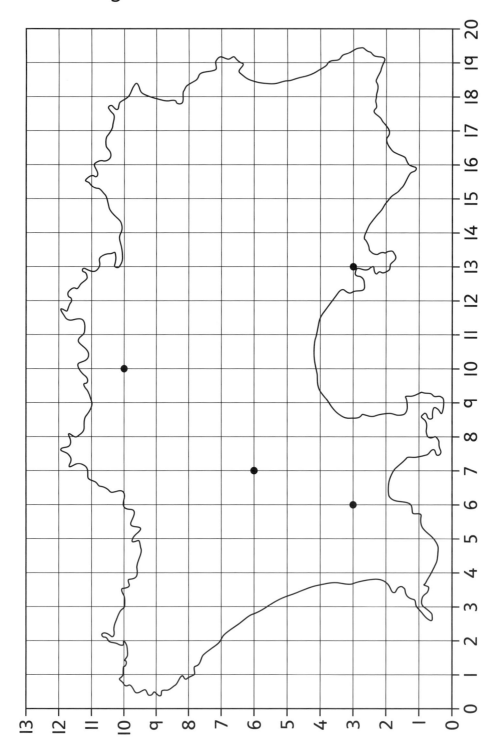

Time facts

Abacus Evolve Year 3 Challenge PCM © Pearson Education Ltd 2009

I day A 12 months	**I day** B 7 days	**I day** C A little over 4 weeks	**I day** D 60 minutes
I year A Half of a fortnight	**I week** B 60 minutes	**I month** C February often has 4 of these	**I hour** D 3 of these make a season
I week A 12 of these in a year	**I hour** B A century has 100 of these	**I week** C 14 days	**I month** D 60 seconds
I month A 60 minutes	**I year** B 60 seconds	**I fortnight** C About 52 weeks	**I minute** D About 52 of these in each year
I hour A 2 weeks	**I minute** B The longest has 31 days	**I year** C 24 of these in a day	**I week** D About 365 days
I fortnight A 7 of these in a week	**I month** B 24 hours	**I hour** C A fortnight has 14 of these	**I year** D April has 30 of these

Logic tracks

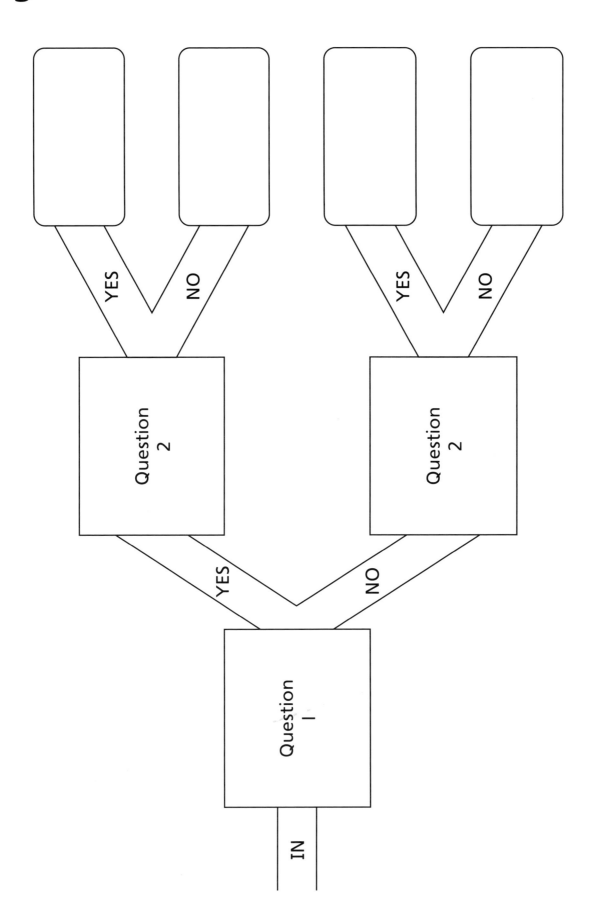

Pentacircles and hexacircles

Pentacircles

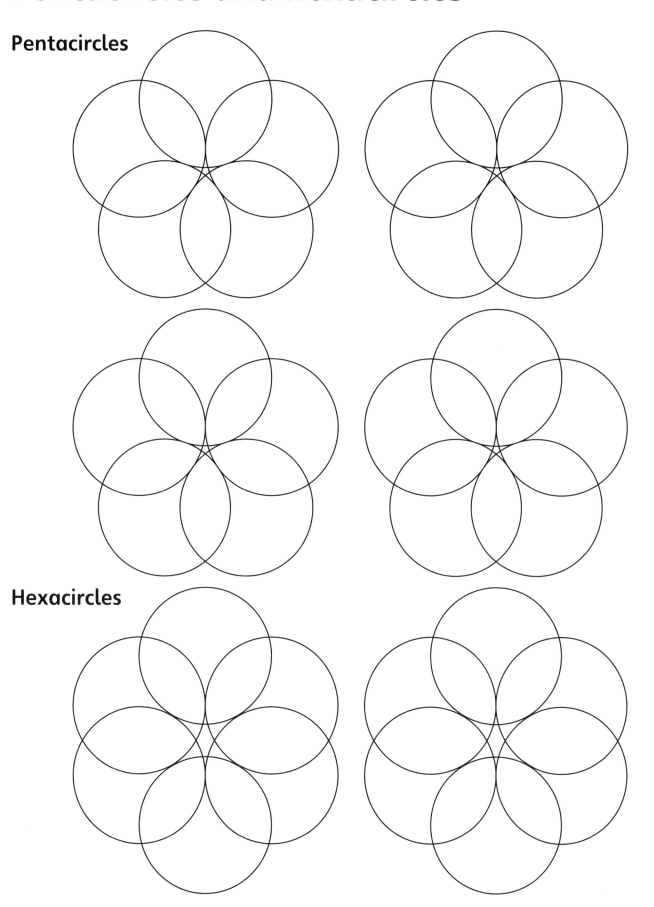

Hexacircles

Abacus Evolve Year 3 Challenge PCM © Pearson Education Ltd 2009

Finding differences

500 A Difference is 175	**500** B Difference is 350	**500** C Difference is 85	**500** D Difference is 270
325 A Difference is 170	**150** B Difference is 80	**415** C Difference is 265	**230** D Difference is 645
155 A Difference is 560	**230** B Difference is 555	**150** C Difference is 795	**875** D Difference is 230
715 A Difference is 385	**785** B Difference is 140	**945** C Difference is 320	**645** D Difference is 495
330 A Difference is 315	**645** B Difference is 230	**625** C Difference is 95	**150** D Difference is 225
645 A Difference is 145	**415** B Difference is 85	**530** C Difference is 30	**375** D Difference is 125

Abacus Evolve Year 3 Challenge PCM © Pearson Education Ltd 2009

Subtracting money amounts

DVDs for sale!	Buying a T-shirt
How much does each DVD cost?	How much money is left?

£2·50 OFF ALL DVD'S

£13·99
£15·99
£12·49
£12·99

How much will I have left if I buy a T-shirt?

£3·99
£4·99
£5·39
£6·99

Discounts

How much money is saved?

How much will I save if I buy…?

SALE

SALE

SALE

Skateboards £35·50 £19·98

Footballs £25·99 £19·50

Goggles £15·49 £12·50

Rackets £65·75 £48·95

Differences

- Use six different digit cards and make two amounts of money.
- Record them, but keep them secret.
- Find the difference between your amounts of money.
- Swap your difference with a partner.
- Can you use each other's difference to work out the six starting digits?

The answer is

£ _____

What was the subtraction?

Multiplication arithmagons

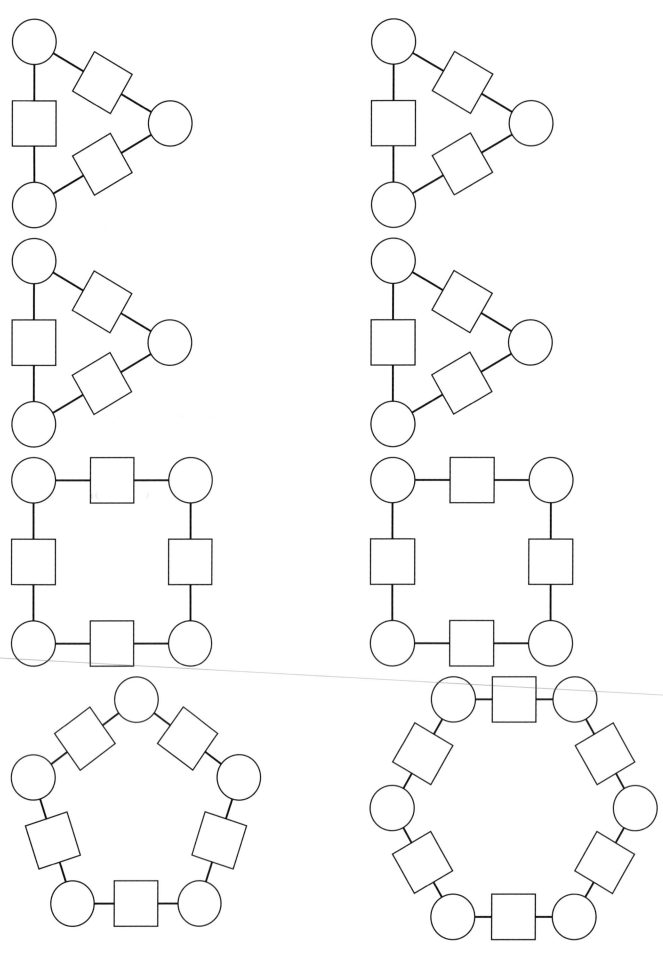

Abacus Evolve Year 3 Challenge PCM © Pearson Education Ltd 2009

Multiplying and dividing by 10, 100 and 1000

70 A $800 \div 10$	**70** B $180 \div 6$	**70** C $8000 \div 1000$	**70** D 500×10
80 A 40×3	**30** B 9×1000	**8** C $4800 \div 80$	**5000** D $3 \cdot 6 \times 100$
120 A $600 \div 30$	**9000** B $500 \div 100$	**60** C $0 \cdot 4 \times 10$	**360** D 100×3
20 A $25 \div 10$	**5** B 3×500	**4** C 2000×4	**300** D $600 \div 20$
2·5 A 40×50	**1500** B $60 \div 100$	**8000** C 40×10	**30** D 90×3
2000 A $350 \div 5$	**0·6** B $7000 \div 100$	**400** C $560 \div 8$	**270** D $0 \cdot 7 \times 100$

Matching fractions cards

$\frac{2}{4}$	$\frac{1}{5}$	$\frac{2}{3}$	$\frac{3}{4}$
$\frac{3}{5}$	$\frac{5}{6}$	$\frac{3}{8}$	$\frac{7}{8}$
$\frac{3}{6}$	$\frac{4}{20}$	$\frac{6}{9}$	$\frac{6}{8}$
$\frac{6}{10}$	$\frac{20}{24}$	$\frac{9}{24}$	$\frac{21}{24}$

Matching money cards

£3·20	£3·17	£3·09	£3·02	£2·96
£2·88	£2·85	£2·81	£2·74	£2·73
97p	94p	89p	86p	83p
79p	77p	76p	72p	67p

Shape totals: triangles

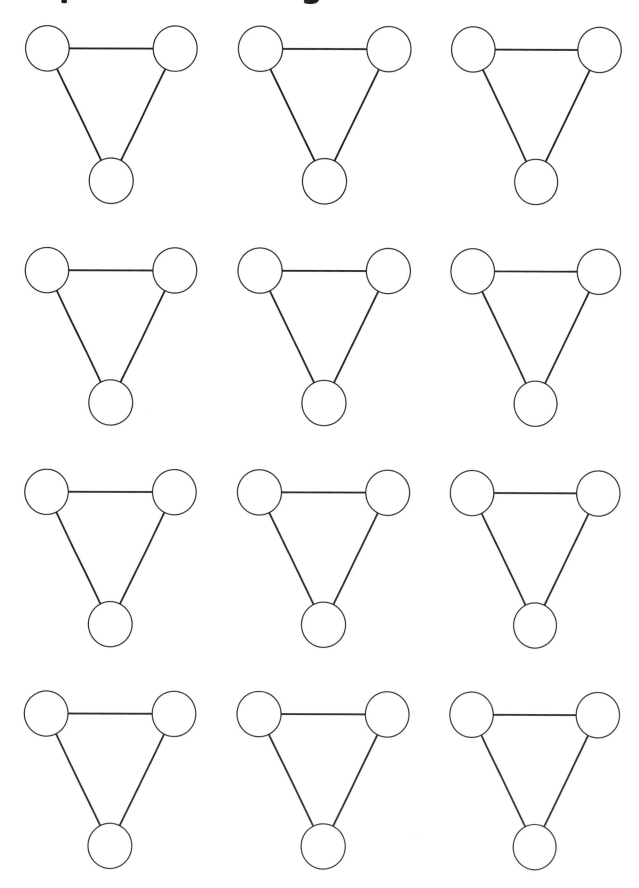

Abacus Evolve Year 3 Challenge PCM © Pearson Education Ltd 2009

Shape totals: squares

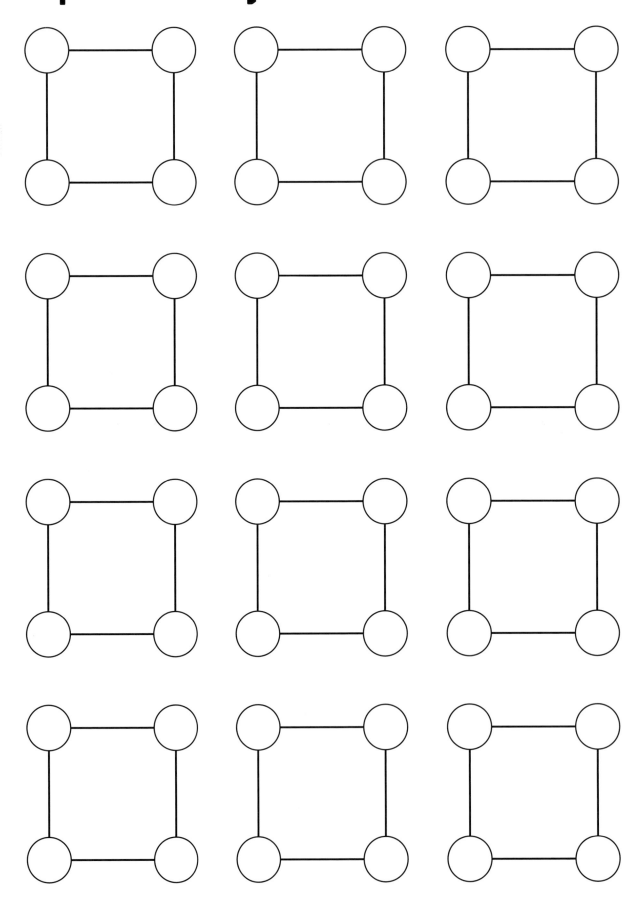

Shape totals: pentagons

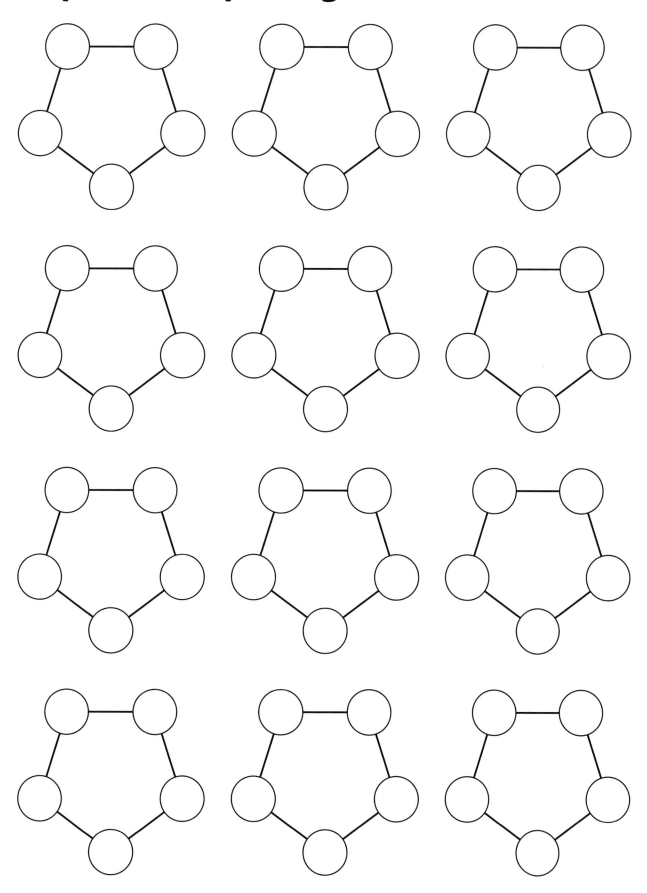

Abacus Evolve Year 3 Challenge PCM © Pearson Education Ltd 2009

Self assessment sheet

	What I did to show this
I planned and completed my work in an organised way.	
I described patterns that I found.	
I made and tested predictions.	
I explained some of my findings, giving reasons.	
I wrote my conclusions looking back at my working.	
Other things I learned in this work.	

Abacus Evolve Year 3 Challenge PCM © Pearson Education Ltd 2009

Diamond totals: 2 by 2 triangles

A diamond is made from two equilateral triangles: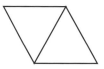

Can you find three diamonds in a 2 by 2 triangle?
Colour one of the diamonds in each copy of the triangle.

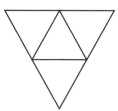 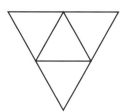 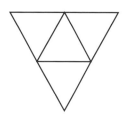

Arrange the numbers 5, 10, 15 and 20 in these
triangles in as many different ways as possible.
What are the diamond totals for each triangle?

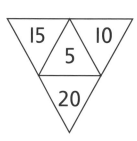

Record your working on PCM F.
Here are some examples to get you started.

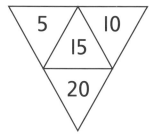 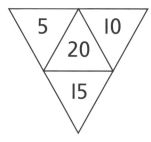 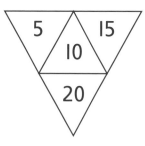

Totals: 20, 25, 35   25, 30, 35   15, 25, 30

Diamond totals: blank 2 by 2 triangles

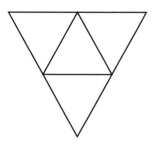 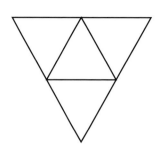 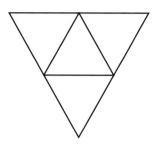

Totals: _____ _____ _____

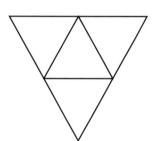 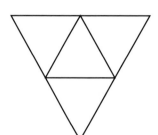 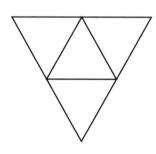

Totals: _____ _____ _____

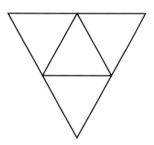 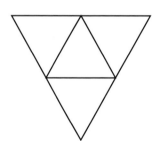 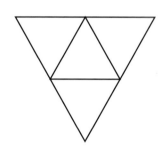

Totals: _____ _____ _____

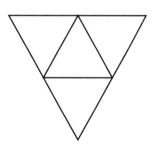 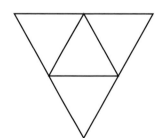 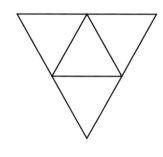

Totals: _____ _____ _____

Diamond totals: 3 by 3 triangles

How many diamonds can you find in a 3 by 3 triangle? They point in three different directions. Colour one type of diamond in each of these three triangles. Use a different colour for each diamond.

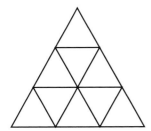 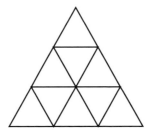 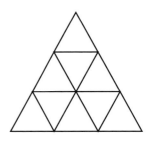

Use these triangles to investigate the questions your teacher will ask you.

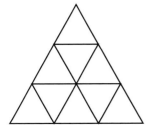 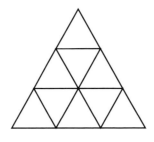 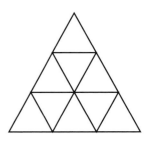

Totals: _____   _____   _____

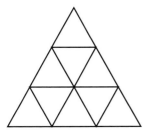 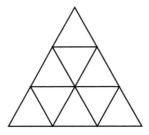 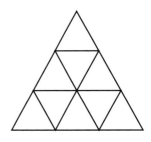

Totals: _____   _____   _____

Abacus **Evolve** Year 3 Challenge PCM © Pearson Education Ltd 2009

Home for gnomes: introduction

Use five cubes to make a home for a gnome that fits on a 3 by 3 plot.
The house must have at least one room upstairs.

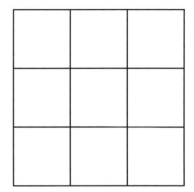

You need to fax your plans to the gnome builder. He will need a bird's eye view, a view from the front, and a view from the side.

The three views for this house are shown below. Make the house and look at it from different directions.

From which directions do you have to look at the house to see the views shown below?

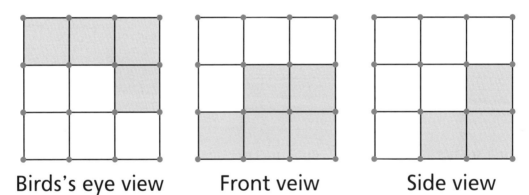

| Birds's eye view | Front veiw | Side view |

Make as many different houses as you can and draw the three views for each on PCM I.

Home for gnomes: views

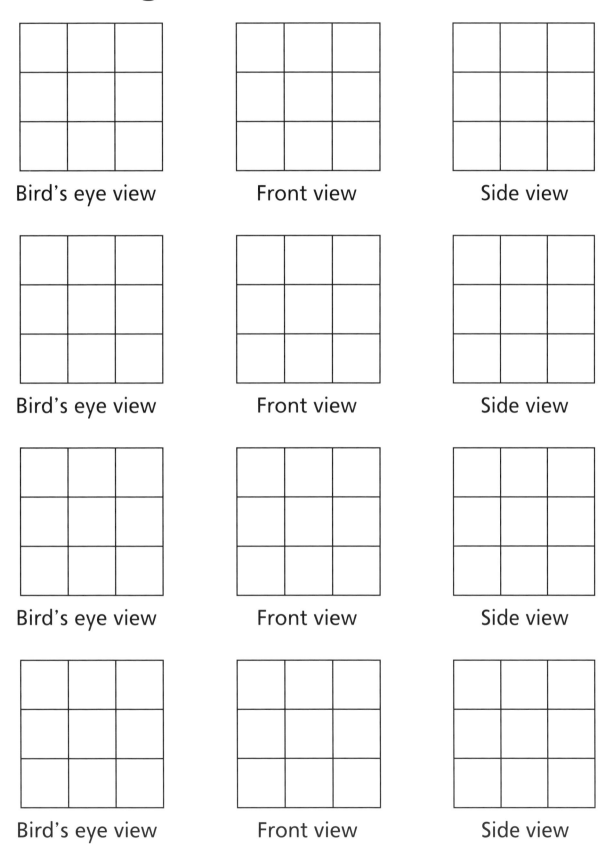

Bird's eye view Front view Side view

Bird's eye view Front view Side view

Bird's eye view Front view Side view

Bird's eye view Front view Side view

Abacus Evolve Year 3 Challenge PCM © Pearson Education Ltd 2009

Home for gnomes: rules

Set 1

The home must have a front and rear garden.

It should not be symmetrical at all.

It should have no more than two storeys.

All rooms must have at least two windows.

Set 2

The home must have a rear garden and a private corner for sitting.

It should not be symmetrical at all.

It should have an overhanging room to provide the roof for a car port.

It must have at least two rooms upstairs.

Set 3

The home must have a front and rear garden with space for a car.

It should be a bungalow.

All rooms must have at least one window.

Answers

AI

AI.I
PCM I

1.
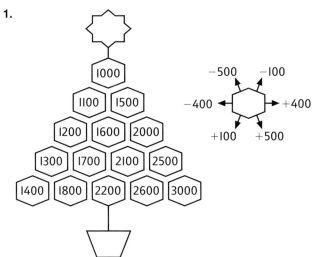

2.
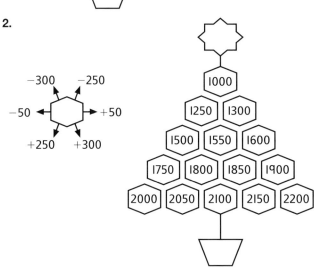

3. Answers will vary.
4. Answers will vary.

Extra

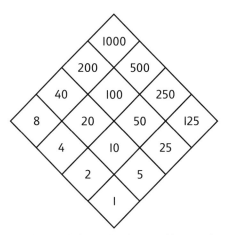

If the start number is 4 then all values will be ×4 those in the grid above.

AI.2
PCM 3

1–100 square and 101–110 square	
pawn	$^+$10, $^+$20 ($^+$11 or $^+$9 when 'taking')
rook	$^+$1, $^-$1, $^+$2, $^-$2,...... $^+$9, $^-$9 $^+$10, $^-$10, $^+$20, $^-$20,......$^+$90, $^-$90
bishop	$^+$11, $^-$11, $^+$22, $^-$22,...... $^+$99, $^-$99 $^+$9, $^-$9, $^+$18, $^-$18,......... $^+$81, $^-$81
queen	$^+$1, $^-$1, $^+$2, $^-$2,...... $^+$9, $^-$9 $^+$10, $^-$10, $^+$20, $^-$20,......$^+$90, $^-$90 $^+$11, $^-$11, $^+$22, $^-$22,...... $^+$99, $^-$99 $^+$9, $^-$9, $^+$18, $^-$18,......... $^+$81, $^-$81
king	$^+$1, $^-$1, $^+$9, $^-$9, $^+$10, $^-$10, $^+$11, $^-$11
knight	$^+$19, $^-$19, $^+$8, $^-$8, $^+$12, $^-$12, $^+$21, $^-$21

PCM 4

5–500 square	
pawn	$^+$50, $^+$100 ($^+$55 or $^+$45 when 'taking')
rook	$^+$5, $^-$5, $^+$10, $^-$10,...... $^+$45, $^-$45 $^+$50, $^-$50, $^+$100, $^-$100,......$^+$450, $^-$450
bishop	$^+$55, $^-$55, $^+$110, $^-$110,...... $^+$495, $^-$495 $^+$45, $^-$45, $^+$90, $^-$90,......... $^+$405, $^-$405
queen	$^+$5, $^-$5, $^+$20, $^-$10,...... $^+$45, $^-$45 $^+$50, $^-$50, $^+$100, $^-$100,......$^+$450, $^-$450 $^+$55, $^-$55, $^+$110, $^-$110,...... $^+$495, $^-$495 $^+$45, $^-$45, $^+$90, $^-$90,......... $^+$405, $^-$405
king	$^+$5, $^-$5, $^+$45, $^-$45, $^+$50, $^-$50, $^+$55, $^-$55
knight	$^+$95, $^-$95, $^+$40, $^-$40, $^+$60, $^-$12, $^+$105, $^-$105

110–900 square	
pawn	$^+$80, $^+$160 ($^+$90 or $^+$70 when 'taking')
rook	$^+$10, $^-$10, $^+$20, $^-$20,...... $^+$70, $^-$70 $^+$80, $^-$80, $^+$160, $^-$160,......$^+$720, $^-$720
bishop	$^+$70, $^-$70, $^+$140, $^-$140,...... $^+$490, $^-$490 $^+$90, $^-$90, $^+$180, $^-$180,......... $^+$630, $^-$630
queen	$^+$10, $^-$10, $^+$20, $^-$20,...... $^+$70, $^-$70 $^+$80, $^-$80, $^+$160, $^-$160......$^+$720, $^-$720 $^+$70, $^-$70, $^+$140, $^-$140,...... $^+$490, $^-$490 $^+$90, $^-$90, $^+$180, $^-$180,......... $^+$630, $^-$630
king	$^+$10, $^-$10, $^+$70, $^-$70, $^+$80, $^-$80, $^+$90, $^-$90
knight	$^+$150, $^-$150, $^+$60, $^-$60, $^+$100, $^-$100, $^+$170, $^-$170

AI.3
PCM 5

1.
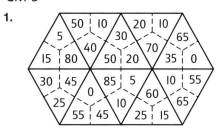

2. Answers will vary.
3. Answers will vary.

AI.4

1. 25p
2. 75p
3. 40p
4. 120p or £1·20
5. 5p, 5p, 5p, 5p, 25p, 25p, 25p, 25p
6. £1, £1, 50p, 50p, 50p
7. £2·50 × 4, £5 × 2
8. £1, 50p, 20p, 20p
9. £5, £2, 20p, 20p
10. £5, £5, £5, £2, £2, 25p, 10p

AI.5

1. Children list numbers   50   100   150   200   250
2. Children list numbers   100   125   150………   500
3. Children list numbers   1000   980   960………   800
4. Children list numbers   5000   4500   4000……   0
5. Answers will vary.
6. Repeated subtraction of 1 gives a 0 in the units place.
   Repeated subtraction of 10 gives a 0 in the tens place.
   Repeated subtraction of 1000 gives a 0 in the thousands place.
7. 20
8. 45-seat: 23 coaches; 32-seat: 32 coaches; 29-seat: 35 coaches.
9. Answers will vary.

Extra

Answers will vary.

AI.6

1.
2.
3.
4.
5.
6.

BI

BI.I

1. Answers will vary.
2. For the ×3 table the second time round is the "first-time" number +30
   For the ×4 table the second time round is the "first-time" number +40
   For the ×5 table the second time round is the "first-time" number +50
   Etc.

Extra

Diagrams show ×3, ×5, ×6, ×7, ×8, ×9

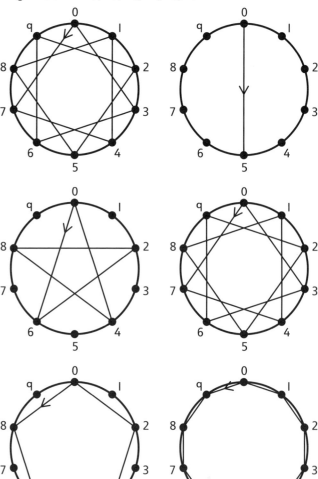

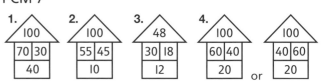

BI.2

PCM 7

1.
```
   100
 70 | 30
   40
```
2.
```
   100
 55 | 45
   10
```
3.
```
   48
 30 | 18
   12
```
4.
```
   100
 60 | 40
   20
```
or
```
   100
 40 | 60
   20
```

5.
```
   73
 62 | 11
   51
```

6. Answers will vary.
7. Answers will vary.
8. Answers will vary.
9. Answers will vary.
10. Answers will vary.

11.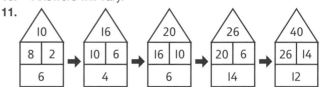
```
   10          16          20          26          40
 8 | 2  →   10 | 6  →   16 | 10  →  20 | 6  →   26 | 14
   6           4           6          14          12
```

12. Answers will vary.

BI.3
PCM 8

1	6	8
5	7	3
9	2	4

1	6	8
9	2	4
5	7	3

5	7	3
1	6	8
9	2	4

1	8	6
5	3	7
9	4	2

1	8	6
9	4	2
5	3	7

5	3	7
1	8	6
9	4	2

6	1	8
7	5	3
2	9	4

6	1	8
2	9	4
7	5	3

7	5	3
6	1	8
2	9	4

BI.4

1.

2.

3.

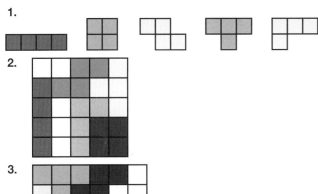

Extra

BI.5

1. Answers will vary.
2. Each tile is rotated 90° ($\frac{1}{4}$ of a turn) clockwise.
3. Answers will vary.

BI.6

1. Answers will vary.
2. Answers will vary.
3. Answers will vary.

CI.1

This is a measuring exercise.

CI.2

This is a measuring exercise.

CI.3
PCM I2

1. $12 + 11 + 3 + 6 + 7 + 24 + 3 + 16 = 82\,km$
2. $11.7 + 10.7 + 3.5 + 6 + 7.2 + 23.7 + 3 + 16.1 = 81.9\,km$
   [0.1 km = 100 m less]
3. Answers will vary.

CI.4

This is a data collection exercise.

CI.5

1.

Stem	Leaves					
5	2	7	7			
6	0	6	9			
7	2	5	7			
8	0	1	2	8	9	
9	0	1	2	4	5	9

2. There were more scores in the 90s than any other.
3. $99 - 52 = 47$
4. There were 2 more scores in the 80s than in the 60s
5. $100 - 72 = 28$; $100 - 75 = 25$; $100 - 77 = 23$

Extra

Leaves			Stem	Leaves		
	2	2	5	7		
		0	6	6	9	
		2	7	5	7	
	2	1 0	8	8	9	
4	2	1 0	9	5	9	

This diagram separates the lower numbers in each ten from the higher numbers in each ten. This could be useful if you were particularly interested in numbers in a certain range.

CI.6

PCM I3

1. and **2.**

square	spider		ant		beetle		woodlouse	
1	ЖЖ I	11	ЖЖ II	12	IIII	4	III	3
2	ЖЖЖ	15	ЖЖ I	11	ЖЖ III	8	IIII	4
3	ЖЖ IIII	14	ЖЖ III	8	ЖЖ II	7	II	2
4	ЖЖЖ III	18	ЖЖ IIII	9	II	2	I	1
5	ЖЖЖ II	17	ЖЖ II	7	ЖЖ I	6	III	3
6	ЖЖЖЖ	20	ЖЖЖ	15	III	3	III	3
7	ЖЖ II	12	ЖЖ	10	ЖЖ IIII	9	II	2
8	ЖЖ III	13	ЖЖ III	8	I	1	ЖЖЖЖ II	22
totals	120		80		40		40	

3.

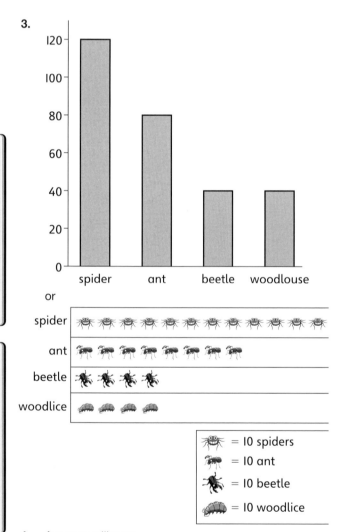

4. Answers will vary.

Extra

Beetles	5 per square metre
Ants	10 per square metre
Woodlice	5 per square metre
Spiders	15 per square metre

DI.1

1. 6 and 7 or 5 and 8
2. Answers will vary.
3. 152 and 148 or 154 and 146
4. For example: one disc 6 and 195, one disc 4 and 205
5. For example: one disc 9 and 339, one disc 8 and 341
6. For example: one disc 4 and 491, one disc 9 and 509
7. For example: one disc 5 and 524, one disc 9 and 476
8. Answers will vary.

Extra

For example: one disc 1 and 3, one disc 3 and 4, one disc 5 and 9

DI.2

PCM I4

This is a game.

Extra

Each row and each column total 20. The four corner numbers add to 20.
Each row and each column total 250. The four corner numbers add to 20.
Each row and each column total 500. The four corner numbers add to 20.
Each row and each column total 1000. The four corner numbers add to 20.

DI.3

PCM I5

1. $143 - 5 = 138$
2. $226 - 9 = 217$
3. $365 - 7 = 358$
4. $256 - 40 = 216$
5. $406 - 50 = 356$
6. $817 - 30 = 787$

7.

A 1	7	B 2	▓	C 9	D 2
0	▓	E 5	6	▓	1
F 9	2	4	▓	G 9	6
0	▓	8	▓	0	▓
H 8	0	▓	I 4	3	2

8. Answers will vary.

DI.4

1. 9:40   1:17
2. Answers will vary.
3. Answers will vary.

DI.5

PCM I6

Set A

How many seconds in 2 minutes?	**120**
How many seconds in 1 min 30 s?	**90**
How many seconds in 1 min 10 s?	**70**
How many seconds in 1 min 40 s?	**100**
How many seconds in 1 min 50 s?	**110**
How many seconds in 1 min 20 s?	**80**

Set B

How many minutes in 1 hour 40 min?	**100**
How many minutes in 1 hour 15 min?	**75**
How many minutes in 1 hour 10 min?	**70**
How many minutes in 1 hour 45 min?	**105**
How many minutes in 3 hours?	**180**
How many minutes in 1 hour 20 min?	**80**

Set C

How many seconds in 3 minutes?	**180**
How many seconds in 2 minutes?	**120**
How many seconds in 1 min 25 s?	**85**
How many seconds in 1 min 15 s?	**75**
How many seconds in 1 min 45 s?	**105**
How many seconds in 1 min 20 s?	**80**

Set D

How many minutes in 1 hour 10 min?	**70**
How many minutes in 3 hours?	**180**
How many minutes in 1 hour 50 min?	**110**
How many minutes in 1 hour 45 min?	**105**
How many minutes in 1 hour 30 min?	**90**
How many minutes in 1 hour 20 min?	**80**

DI.6

1. 11:20   12:40
2. 11:40   1:20
3. 1:40
4. 10:10
5. 3:05
6. 8:40

7. There are other possible correct solutions.

Start time	Number of minutes	End time
11:45	23 minutes earlier	12:08
11:55	18 minutes earlier	11:37
12:15	13 minutes earlier	12:02
12:25	33 minutes later	12:58
11:45	18 minutes later	1:03
11:45	18 minutes earlier	11:27
11:45	23 minutes later	12:08
12:35	13 minutes later	12:48
12:15	18 minutes earlier	11:57
12:35	23 minutes later	12:58

EI.I

PCM I8

1. $6 \times 3 = 3 \times 6 = 18$; $18 \div 6 = 3$; $18 \div 3 = 6$
2. $8 \times 3 = 3 \times 8 = 24$; $24 \div 8 = 3$; $24 \div 3 = 8$

Extra

Set A

24 divide by 8   **3** multiply by 5   **15** divide by 3
5 multiply by 4   **20** divide by 5   **4** multiply by 6 **24**

Set B

24 divide by 6   **4** multiply by 5   **20** divide by 4
5 multiply by 3   **15** divide by 5   **3** multiply by 8 **24**

Set C

24 divide by 3   **8** multiply by 4   **32** divide by 8
4 multiply by 3   **12** divide by 2   **6** multiply by 4 **24**

Set D

24 divide by 4   **6** multiply by 2   **12** divide by 3
4 multiply by 8   **32** divide by 4   **8** multiply by 3 **24**

EI.2

1.

×	2	3
2	4	6
4	8	12

2.

×	3	5
2	6	10
5	15	25

3.

×	2	4
2	4	8
6	12	24

4.

×	2	3	4
2	4	6	8
3	6	9	12
4	8	12	16

5.

×	5	10	15
2	10	20	30
3	15	30	45
4	20	40	60

6.

×	3	5	8
4	12	20	32
6	18	30	48
8	24	40	64

7. Answers will vary.
8. Answers will vary.

Extra

Answers will vary.

DI

EI

EI.3

1. $13 \times 2 = 26$
2. $34 \times 2 = 68$
3. $41 \times 3 = 123$
4. $12 \times 4 = 48$
5. Answers will vary.
6. $14 \times 5 = 70$ $15 \times 4 = 60$ $41 \times 5 = 205$
   $45 \times 1 = 45$ $51 \times 4 = 204$ $54 \times 1 = 54$
7. Answers will vary. For three digits $a < b < c$ the largest product is always made by $ba \times c$ and the smallest by $bc \times a$
8. Answers will vary.
9. Answers will vary.

EI.4

1. $\frac{1}{2}$ of $50 = 25$ $\frac{1}{2}$ of $10 = 5$ $\frac{1}{5}$ of $10 = 2$
2. $\frac{1}{4}$ of $12 = 3$
3. Answers will vary.
4. $\frac{1}{2}$ of $24 = 12$ $\frac{1}{3}$ of $24 = 8$ $\frac{1}{4}$ of $24 = 6$
   $\frac{1}{6}$ of $24 = 4$ $\frac{1}{8}$ of $24 = 4$ $\frac{1}{12}$ of $24 = 2$
5. Answers will vary.
6. Answers will vary.

Extra

For example:

$\frac{1}{6}$ of $24 = 4$ $\frac{2}{6}$ of $24 = 8$ $\frac{3}{6}$ of $24 = 12$
$\frac{4}{6}$ of $24 = 16$ $\frac{5}{6}$ of $24 = 20$

EI.5

PCM 19

For example:

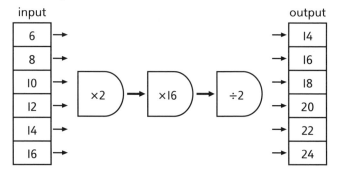

EI.6

PCM 20

1. Answers will vary.
2. For example
   Enlarge area by a factor of 2 each time changes the orientation of the shape.

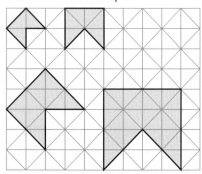

Extra

For example:

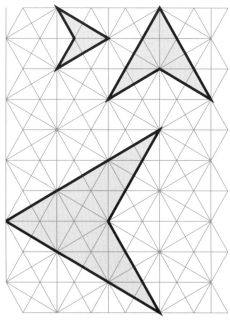

The areas are 4, 12, 36 triangles. The orientation changes at each scaling.

A2.1

1. 7370   nearest 10
   7400   nearest 100
   7500   nearest 500
   7000   nearest 1000
2. 5490   5500   5500   5000
3. 23
4. 140
5. 20
6. 225   274
7. 775   824
8. 4725   4774
9. 74 cm
10. 1 m 4 cm
11. 554 cm
12. £195
13. £815
14. £425

A2.2

1. 2198   2222   3167   3189   3204
2. £10·49   £10·96   £11·01   £11·12   £11·45
3. Any number from 45 211 to 45 218
4. Any number from 13 490 to 14 502
5. Any number from 67 676 to 76 681
6. Any number from 10 706 to 11 697
7. 259
8. 394
9. 1433
10. 6199
    The rule to find half-way number is add the numbers together and halve the answer.

PCM 21

Set A

The largest number from 144, 142, 1044	**1044**
A number between 230 and 290	**256**
The smallest number from 342, 321, 330	**321**
Exactly half-way between 1091 and 1015	**1053**
The largest number from 199, 218, 225	**225**
A number between 90 and 105	**100**

Set B

The largest number from 256, 240, 252	**256**
The smallest number from 225, 239, 227	**225**
The smallest number from 105, 110, 103	**103**
A number between 3301 and 3339	**3321**
A number between 1354 and 1501	**144**
The largest number from 87, 100, 97	**100**

Set C

The largest number from 321, 300, 319	**321**
Exactly half-way between 280 and 232	**256**
A number between 2003 and 2504	**2225**
Exactly half-way between 135 and 153	**144**
The largest number from 103, 99, 102	**103**
Exactly half-way between 93 and 107	**100**

Set D

A number between 9190 and 9120	**9103**
Exactly half-way between 350 and 292	**321**
The smallest number from 146, 144, 151	**144**
Exactly half-way between 6210 and 6240	**6225**
The smallest number from 264, 270, 256	**256**
The smallest number from 100, 123, 102	**100**

A2.3

Answers will vary.

Extra

Children can amend their historic dates in this way for each calendar:

+2698 for Chinese calendar
+3760 for Hebrew calendar
+3101 for Indian calendar
−580 for Islamic calendar

A2.4

1. 100 110 120 130 140 150 160 170 180 190 200
2. 200 205 210 215 220 225 230 235 240 245 250
3. 500 450 400 350 300 250 200 150 100 50 0
4. 1000 900 800 700 600 500 400 300 200 100 0
5. 45 545 1045 1545 2045 2545 3045 3545 4045
    4545 5045
6. 9075 8075 7075 6075 5075 4075 3075 2075
    1075 75
7. Answers will vary.
8. Answers will vary.
9. Answers will vary.
10. Answers will vary.
11. Answers will vary.

A2.5

PCM 22

Answers will vary.

Set W

£11·54 + £5 − 50p − 5p	**£15·99**
£15·99 + £5 + 50p	**£21·49**
£21·49 + £5 + £1 + 50p	**£27·99**
£27·99 + £5 − £1	**£31·99**

Set X

£24·28 + £1 + 10p + 10p + 5p	**£25·33**
£25·33 + £10 − £1 − £1 + 50p − 5p	**£33·78**
£33·78 + £5 + 5p	**£38·83**
£38·83 + £1 + 50p	**£40·33**

Set Y

£49·35 + 50p + 10p + 5p	**£50·00**
£50·00 + £5 − 50p − 10p	**£54·40**
£54·40 + 50p − 5p	**£54·85**
£54·85 + £5 + 10p	**£59·95**

Set Z

£18·74 + £5 + £1 − 5p	**£24·69**
£24·69 + £5 − 50p + 5p	**£29·24**
£29·24 + £1 − 5p	**£30·19**
£30·19 + £10 − 50p	**£39·69**

A2.6

1. The total of each ring is 125
2.

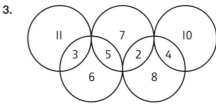

3.

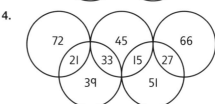

4.

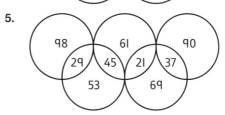

5.

90 is the missing number

6.

This number 90 is not needed.

7. Answers will vary.

B2

B2.1

1. 85
2. 45
3. 70
4. 45
5. 95
6. 20
7. Answers will vary.
8. 88
9. 49
10. 69
11. 46
12. 96
13. 23
14. 28
15. 36
16. 66
17. Answers will vary.

Extra

1914	86 years before 2000
1953	47 years before 2000
1966	34 years before 2000
1989	11 years before 2000

Actual answers will depend on the date children attempt this task.

B2.2

1. 700
2. 90
3. 340
4. 730
5. 10 + 190   20 + 180   30 + 170   40 + 160   50 + 150
   60 + 140   70 + 130   80 + 120   90 + 110   100 + 100
6. £5 − £3·99 = £1·01   total in purse £4·22
7. £1 − 45p = 55p   total in purse £5·60
8. £10 − £7·25 = £2·25   total in purse £2·59
9. £10 − £6·50 = £3·50   total in purse £14·70
10. £1 − 66p = 34p   total in purse £5·89
11. £5 − £2·20 = £2·80   total in purse £3·05
12. Answers will vary.

Extra

Answers will vary.

B2.3

PCM 24

Set A

From 560, make 1000.	440
From 70p, how many pence to make £1?	30
From 20, make 100.	80
From 280, make 1000.	720
From £1·50, how many pence to make £10?	850
From 76, make 100.	24

Set B

From £2·80, how many pence to make £10?	720
From 40, make 100	60
From £9·20, how many pence to make £10?	80
From 65p, how many pence to make £1?	35
From 40p, how many 10p pieces to make £1?	6
From 76p, how many pence to make £1?	24

Set C

From 400p, how many pounds to make £10?	6
From £5·60, how many pence to make £10?	440
From £7, how many 10p pieces to make £10?	30
From £4, how many 10p pieces to make £10?	60
From £6·50, how many 10p pieces to make £10?	35
From 760, how many tens to make 1000?	24

Set D

From £2, how many 10p pieces to make £10	80
From £7, how many 50p pieces to make £10?	6
From 150, make 1000.	850
From 65, make 100.	35
From 70, make 100.	30
From £9·76, how many pence to make £10?	24

B2.4

1. Yes there are 6 lines of symmetry. Three others bisect the sides.
2. For a regular polygon with n sides there are n lines of symmetry.
3. 6
4. There is always 1 more plane of symmetry in the prism than the number of lines of symmetry of the cross-section.

5.

	Vertices	Faces
Start with a hexagonal prism:	12	8
Add a hexagonal-based pyramid:	13	13
Add a hexagonal-based pyramid:	14	18
Add a square-based pyramid:	15	21
Add a square-based pyramid:	16	24
Add a square-based pyramid:	17	27
Add a square-based pyramid:	18	30
Add a square-based pyramid:	19	33
Add a square-based pyramid:	20	36

6. A regular pentagonal prism would generate a star with 17 vertices and 30 faces.

Extra

A cube has 9 planes of symmetry.

B2.5

1.

2. Answers will vary.
3. Answers will vary.
4. Children's own constructions.

B2.6

PCM 25

1. Answers will vary.
2. Triangular prism; add a square to give an anti-prism; hexagonal prism with one extra face.
3. They both have 10 vertices and two pentagonal faces. The prism has 7 faces with other faces rectangular, the anti-prism has 12 faces with oither faces triangular.
4. They both have 10 vertices.
5. They both have planes of symmetry based on the lines of symmetry of the pentagonal face

6. **Prisms**

Base polygon	Vertices	Edges	Faces
Equilateral triangle	6	9	5
Square	8	12	6
Regular pentagon	10	15	7
Regular hexagon	12	18	8

Anti-prisms

Base polygon	Vertices	Edges	Faces
Equilateral triangle	6	12	8
Square	8	16	10
Regular pentagon	10	20	12
Regular hexagon	12	24	14

7. The prisms have $1\frac{1}{2}$ times as many edges as vertices. The number of faces is the number of sides of the base polygon, plus 2. The anti-prisms have twice as many edges as vertices. The number of faces is two times the number of sides of the base polygon, plus 2.

Extra

This polyhedron has 20 equilateral triangle faces. It is called an icosahedron.

C2.1

This is a measuring exercise.

C2.2

1. 1500 ml
2. 1250 ml
3. 2 ℓ
4. $\frac{3}{4}$ ℓ
5. True
6. False. 300 ml × 9 = 2700 ml = 2·7 ℓ
7. True
8. Two 1·5 litre and two 200 ml
9. 50 ml, 100 ml, 200 ml, 200 ml, 250 ml, 300 ml, 500 ml, 700 ml, 750 ml, 1 litre, 1·25 litres, 1·5 litres, 1·5 litres, 2 litres, 2·5 litres.
10. 100 ml − 50 ml = 50 ml
200 ml − 100 ml = 100 ml
200 ml − 200 ml = 0 ml
250 ml − 200 ml = 50 ml
300 ml − 250 ml = 50 ml
500 ml − 300 ml = 200 ml
700 ml − 500 ml = 200 ml
750 ml − 700 ml = 50 ml
1 litre − 750 ml = 250 ml
1·25 litres − 1 litre = 250 ml
1·5 litres − 1·25 litres = 250 ml
1·5 litres − 1·5 litres = 0 ml
2 litres − 1·5 litres = 500 ml
2·5 litres − 2 litres = 500 ml

Extra

	number of 100 ml bottles	number of 150 ml bottles
1 litre container	10	6
1·5 litre container	15	10
2 litre container	20	13
5 litre container	50	33
10 litre container	100	66

C2.3

1. Men: 108·5 minutes;   Women 118·5 minutes
2. 10 minutes
3. 10 minutes 4 seconds
4. Men: 124 minutes;   Women 135·5 minutes
5. 11·5 minutes
6. 11 minutes 26 seconds
7. Men: 9·7 seconds   Women 10·5 seconds
8. 0·8 seconds
9. 0·8 seconds
10. Men: 43·2 seconds   Women 47·6 seconds
11. 4·4 seconds
12. 4·42 seconds
13. 17 minutes 26 seconds
14. 295 days (2008 was a leap year)

Extra

64 clubs in round 3
32 clubs in round 4
16 clubs in round 5
 8 clubs in round 6
 4 clubs in round 7
 2 clubs in round 8 (the final)

6 matches played: $90 \times 6 = 540$ minutes $= 9$ hours

C2.4

PCM 27

number of species recorded	number of birdwatchers
1–5	10
6–10	5
11–15	6
16–20	15

number of species recorded	number of birdwatchers
1–2	4
3–4	3
5–6	5
7–8	2
9–10	1
11–12	1
13–14	3
15–16	4
17–18	2
19–20	11

C2.5

1. The range is 2 min 30 s
2. See answer for PCM 28
3. The fastest time is 29 min 54 s
   The slowest time is 32 min 24 s
4. The median is 31 min 12 s
5. The lower quartile is 30 min 37 s
   The upper quartile is 31 min 40 s
6. The interquartile range is 1 min 3 s

PCM 28

Times for women's 10 000 m race

Times for women's 10 000 m race

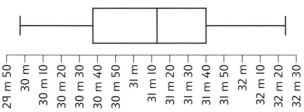

Extra

The winner's time is 13 min.
The range is 1 min.
The median is 13 min 24 s.
The lower quartile is 13 min 10 s.
The upper quartile is 13 min 30 s.
The interquartile range is 13 min 20 s.

C2.6

1. and **2.**

Star name

Number of letters	Frequency
4	1
5	1
6	2
7	3
8	0
9	8
10	1
11	3
12	3
13	2
14	3
15	1

Real name

Number of letters	Frequency
9	1
10	1
11	5
12	3
13	6
14	7
15	1
16	1
17	0
18	1
19	1
20	1

3

Letters in star names

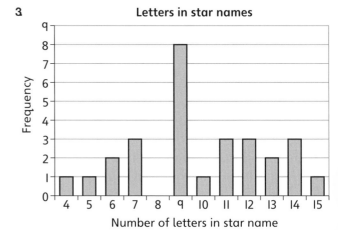

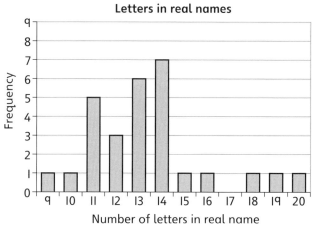

Letters in real names

(Bar chart: x-axis "Number of letters in real name" from 9 to 20, y-axis "Frequency" from 0 to 9)

4. Yes. Only Elle MacPherson and Queen Latifah have more letters in their star name.
5. 9 letters
6. 14 letters
7. Shortest is 4 letters (Pink), longest is 15 (Jennifer Aniston)
8. Shortest is 9 letters (Dana Owens) longest is 20 (Jennifer Anastassakis)

Extra

Difference in number of letters in real and star name	Frequency
0	4
1	1
2	5
3	2
4	2
5	4
6	4
7	5
8	1

D2

D2.1

1. 760
2. 787
3. 793
4. 792
5. 751
6. 733
7. 719
8. Answers will vary.
9. 1295
10. 1245
11. 1292
12. 1219
13. Answers will vary.

D2.2

PCM 31

1., 2.

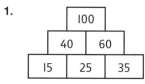

3. Four squares drawn inside the original square.
4. Answers will vary.
5. Answers will vary.

Extra

Shapes with odd numbers of sides do not always get to zero.

D2.3

PCM 32

1.
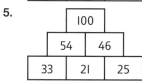

2. Answers will vary.
3. Answers will vary.
4.

5.

6.
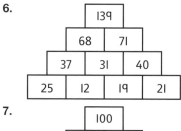

7.
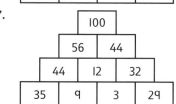

8. Answers will vary.
9. Answers will vary.

C2

D2

10. Largest possible top number 424; smallest possible 232. The top number is always 3 × (sum of middle two bottom bricks) + sum of two outside bottom bricks so the following will all give 424
9, 49, 81, 25 or 9, 81, 49, 25 or 25, 81, 49, 9 or 25, 49, 81, 9

Extra

The two outside bottom bricks must total 40

D2.4

PCM 33

Set A

1500 + 300	1800 + 700	2500 − 400
2100 + 600	2700 − 1500	1200 + 300	**1500**

Set B

1500 + 1200	2700 − 1800	900 + 1200
2100 − 500	1600 halve it	800 + 700	**1500**

Set C

1500 − 600	900 double it	1800 − 600
1200 + 2400	3600 − 2000	1600 − 100	**1500**

Set D

1500 + 600	2100 − 1300	800 double it
1600 + 2000	3600 − 1100	2500 − 1000	**1500**

D2.5

PCM 34

1.

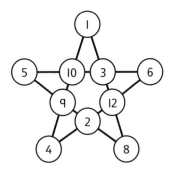

2. Not used 7 and 11. The magic number is 24
3.

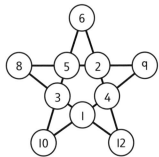

The magic number is 24.
4. Answers will vary. The lines must add to 28
5. Answers will vary. The lines must add to 26.

D2.6

PCM 35

For example:

1.
2.
3.

number	123	137	248	999
number + 99	222	236	347	1098
number − 99	24	38	149	900

---

4. Digital roots   6, 2, 5, 9
5. Digital roots question 2   6, 2, 5, 9
    Digital roots question 3   6, 2, 5, 9
6. Adding 98 gives digital roots   5, 1, 4, 8
    The digital root decreases by 1
    Subtracting 98 gives digital roots   7, 3, 6, 1
    The digital root increases by 1
7. Digital root is unchanged by adding or subtracting any multiple of 9.

E2

E2.1

PCM 36

Set A

60	divide by 6	**10**	multiply by 3	**30**	divide by 5	**6**
	multiply by 12	**72**	divide by 6	**12**	multiply by 5	**60**

Set B

60	divide by 5	**12**	multiply by 6	**72**	divide by 2	**36**
	divide by 6	**6**	multiply by 5	**30**	multiply by 2	**60**

Set C

60	divide by 4	**15**	multiply by 6	**90**	divide by 9	**10**
	multiply by 4	**40**	divide by 2	**20**	multiply by 3	**60**

Set D

60	divide by 10	**6**	multiply by 9	**54**	divide by 6	**9**
	multiply by 10	**90**	divide by 6	**15**	multiply by 4	**60**

E2.2

PCM 37

Range	Living thing
0·1–0·9 nm	amino acid
1–9 nm	DNA
10–99 nm	cold virus
100–999 nm	bacteria (small)
1–9 micron	red blood cell
10–99 microns	pollen grain
0·1–0.9 mm	bacteria (large)
1–9 mm	ant
1–9 cm	bee hummingbird
10–99 cm	koala, giant millipede
1–9 m	elephant, ostrich, giant clam, human
10–99 m	blue whale

1. Bee hummingbird
2. Giant millipede, koala
3. See table above
4. Large bacteria
5. Red blood cells
6. See table above
7. Koala, giant millipede
8. elephant, ostrich, giant clam, human
9. bee hummingbird
10. ant
11. any two things 6 rows apart in the table, for example red blood cell and elephant

E2.3

1. 13
2. 23
3. 12×3
4. Answers will vary.
5. 45
6. 34
7. 35
8. 16
9. 16
10. 11
11. 11

The answers to questions 8 and 9, 10 and 11 are the same as multiplication is the opposite (inverse) of division.

Extra

Answers will vary.

E2.4

1.

1	2	3	4	5	6	7	8	9	10
11	12	13	14	15	16	17	18	19	20
21	22	23	24	25	26	27	28	29	30
31	32	33	34	35	36	37	38	39	40
41	42	43	44	45	46	47	48	49	50
51	52	53	54	55	56	57	58	59	60
61	62	63	64	65	66	67	68	69	70
71	72	73	74	75	76	77	78	79	80
81	82	83	84	85	86	87	88	89	90
91	92	93	94	95	96	97	98	99	100

2. 3, 15, 21, 33, 39, 51, 57, 69, 75, 87, 93
3. 6, 12, 24, 30, 42, 48, 60, 66, 78, 84, 96
4. 9, 27, 45, 63, 81, 99
5. 18, 36, 54, 72, 90
6. 30 blue and black, 60 blue and black, 90 blue, black and red
7. 33 blue, 63 blue and red, 93 blue
8. 27 blue and red, 57 blue, 87 blue

Extra

701 – 800 square has similar patterns but starting in a different place. 702 has blue, black and red stripes
1201 – 1300 square has exactly the same pattern as 1 – 100 square

E2.5

1. 13
2. 28
3. 31
4. 11
5. 12
6. 33

7. The shaded numbers escape the '×3 + 1' flowchart.

1	2	3	4	5	6	7	8	9	10
11	12	13	14	15	16	17	18	19	20
21	22	23	24	25	26	27	28	29	30
31	32	33	34	35	36	37	38	39	40
41	42	43	44	45	46	47	48	49	50
51	52	53	54	55	56	57	58	59	60
61	62	63	64	65	66	67	68	69	70
71	72	73	74	75	76	77	78	79	80
81	82	83	84	85	86	87	88	89	90
91	92	93	94	95	96	97	98	99	100

The shaded numbers escape the '×3 − 1' flowchart.

1	2	3	4	5	6	7	8	9	10
11	12	13	14	15	16	17	18	19	20
21	22	23	24	25	26	27	28	29	30
31	32	33	34	35	36	37	38	39	40
41	42	43	44	45	46	47	48	49	50
51	52	53	54	55	56	57	58	59	60
61	62	63	64	65	66	67	68	69	70
71	72	73	74	75	76	77	78	79	80
81	82	83	84	85	86	87	88	89	90
91	92	93	94	95	96	97	98	99	100

E2.6

1. $\frac{3}{12} = \frac{1}{4}$
2. $\frac{3}{18} = \frac{1}{6}$
3. $\frac{3}{24} = \frac{1}{8}$
4. $\frac{6}{12} = \frac{1}{2}, \frac{6}{18} = \frac{1}{3}, \frac{6}{24} = \frac{1}{4}$
5. Answers will vary.
6. $13 > 12$
7. $9 < 10$
8. $18 > 16$
9. $14 > 11$
10. £2.33 $>$ £2.32
11. £8.75 $<$ £8.80

Extra

$\frac{1}{10}$ of £60 = £6

$\frac{1}{6}$ of £60 = £10

$\frac{1}{5}$ of £60 = $\frac{2}{10}$ of £60 = £12

$\frac{1}{4}$ of £60 = £15

$\frac{3}{10}$ of £60 = £18

$\frac{1}{3}$ of £60 = £20 = $\frac{2}{6}$ of £60 = £20

$\frac{2}{5}$ of £60 = $\frac{4}{10}$ of £60 = £24

$\frac{1}{2}$ of £60 = $\frac{2}{4}$ of £60 = $\frac{3}{6}$ of £60 = $\frac{5}{10}$ of £60 = £30

$\frac{3}{5}$ of £60 = $\frac{6}{10}$ of £60 = £36

$\frac{2}{3}$ of £60 = $\frac{4}{6}$ of £60 = £40

$\frac{7}{10}$ of £60 = £42

$\frac{3}{4}$ of £60 = £45

$\frac{4}{5}$ of £60 = $\frac{8}{10}$ of £60 = £48

$\frac{5}{6}$ of £60 = £50

$\frac{9}{10}$ of £60 = £54

A3

A3.I

PCM 40

Answers will vary.

A3.2

1. 50 + 90 = 140
2. 60 + 90 = 150
3. 80 + 50 = 130
4. £4 + £1 = £5
5. £8 + £3 = £11
6. £7 + £3 = £10
7. Answers will vary. Numbers round as follows.

419 → 420	326 → 330	457 → 460
286 → 290	694 → 690	126 → 130
438 → 440	164 → 160	
73 → 70	47 → 50	61 → 60
43 → 40	82 → 80	58 → 60
71 → 70	38 → 40	

8. Answers will vary.
9. Answers will vary. Numbers round as follows.

£3·23 → £3.20	£1·88 → £1.90	£8·12 → £8.10
£4·87 → £4.90	£9·29 → £9.30	£5·76 → £5.80
£3·75 → £3.80	£5·21 → £5.20	
62p → 60p	37p → 40p	74p → 70p
49p → 50p	95p → £1	28p → 30p
53p → 50p	86p → 90p	

10. Answers will vary.
11. Game. Answers will vary.

Extra

Answers will vary.

A3.3

Answers will vary, for example
1. Step 1: 460, 890, 730

   Step 2: 460 + 890 = 1350   460 + 730 = 1190

   890 + 730 = 1620

   Step 3: 890 − 460 = 430   730 − 460 = 270

   890 − 730 = 160

2. Step 1: 1350, 1190, 430

   Step 2: 1350 + 1190 = 2540   1350 + 430 = 1780

   1190 + 430 = 1620

   Step 3: 1350 − 1190 = 160   1350 − 430 = 920

   1190 − 430 = 760

   There are two answers the same in additions (1620) and subtractions (160)

   The answers to two subtractions add up to make the answer to the third

A3.4

1. Add the two previous answers together to get the next number.
2. 1, 1, 2, 3, 5, 8, 13, 21, 34, 55, 89, 144
3. Answers will vary.
4. 5, 6, 11, 17
5. 2, 10, 12, 22
6. 8, 11, 19, 30
7. 1, 10, 11, 21
8. 7, 15, 22, 37, 59
9. 7, 16, 23, 39, 62
10. 8, 28, 36, 64, 100

Extra

1

1

2 (multiple of 2)

3 (multiple of 3)

5

8 (multiple of 2) (multiple of 4)

13

21 (multiple of 3)

34 (multiple of 2)

55

89

144 (multiple of 2) (multiple of 3) (multiple of 4)

233

377

610 (multiple of 2)

897 (multiple of 3)

Every third number is a multiple of 2

Every fourth number is a multiple of 3

Every fifth number is a multiple of 5

Every sixth number is a multiple of 4

A3.5

1. 18
2. 52
3. 70
4. 7
5. 13
6. 21
7.

Input	Output
50	101
24	49
37	75
193	387
or 96	193
289	579
or 144	289

8. Answers will vary.

A3.6

1–5 Answers will vary.

6–8

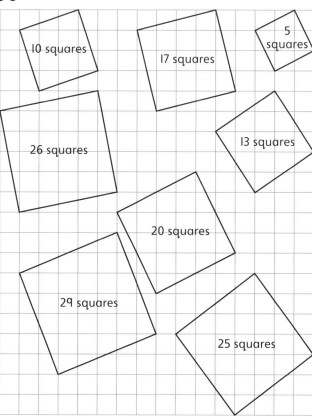

Extra

The areas will be in the ratio 1:2, for example
Areas 6.5 squares and 13 squares

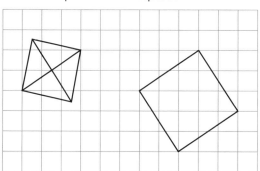

B3.1

PCM 42

	×2	×4	×8	×16
1	2	4	8	16
2	4	8	16	32
3	6	12	24	48
4	8	16	32	64
5	10	20	40	80
6	12	24	48	96
7	14	28	56	112
8	16	32	64	128
9	18	36	72	144
10	20	40	80	160
11	22	44	88	176
12	24	48	96	192
13	26	52	104	208
14	28	56	112	224
15	30	60	120	240

20 × 4 = 80	23 × 4 = 92	25 × 4 = 100	29 × 4 = 116	36 × 4 = 144
20 × 8 = 160	23 × 8 = 184	25 × 8 = 200	29 × 8 = 232	36 × 8 = 288

296 ÷ 8 = 37
328 ÷ 8 = 41
264 ÷ 8 = 33
216 ÷ 8 = 27
140 ÷ 4 = 35
84 ÷ 4 = 21
196 ÷ 4 = 49
176 ÷ 8 = 22
128 ÷ 4 = 32
96 ÷ 4 = 24

B3.2

PCM 43

	A 1	6	B 8		C 1
D 2	0		E 2	F 3	2
G 6	4			H 1	8
I 1	0	J 4		K 6	0
2		L 8	4	0	

A 2	2	B 1		C 9	D 6
			E 6	4	3
F 7	2	0		G 4	2
3		8		1	
H 6	1		I 2	6	4

B3.3

PCM 44

The second picture is 2 × the original. The third picture is 4 × the original.

1.

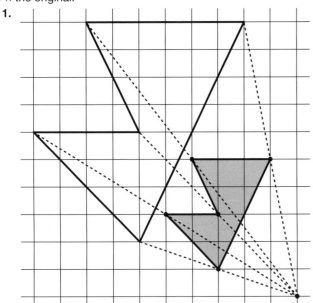

2. Answers will vary.

3. Answers will vary.

Extra

The enlarged shape is also rotated, for example

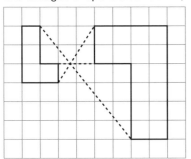

B3.4

1. 90°
2. 30°
3. 45°
4. 120°
5. Answers will vary.
6. 90°
7. 180°
8. 270°
9. 60°
10. 210°
11. 330°
12. 120°
13. 240°

Extra

1 week = 7 days

Hour hand moves 2 complete turns per day.

$14 \times 360 = 5040°$

1 day = 24h Minute hand moves 24 complete turns.

$24 \times 360 = 8640°$

Minute hand moves most.

B3.5

PCM 45

1. 2 spaces east; 1 space south; 1 space south-west; 1 space north-west; 1 space east; 1 space north-west OR 1 space south-east; 1 space west; 1 space south east; 1 space north-east; 1 space north; 2 spaces west.

2. $\frac{1}{2}$, 1, $1\frac{1}{2}$, 1, $\frac{1}{2}$, $3\frac{1}{2}$ right-angles.

Question 3, 4, 5 Children may start in different places and/or go anti-clockwise

3.

direction	number of right-angles
3 spaces east	
1 space south-west	$\frac{1}{2}$
1 space south	$2\frac{1}{2}$
1 space south-east	$2\frac{1}{2}$
3 spaces west	$\frac{1}{2}$
1 space north-east	$\frac{1}{2}$
1 space north	$1\frac{1}{2}$
1 space north-west	$1\frac{1}{2}$
	$\frac{1}{2}$

4.

direction	number of right-angles
1 space south-east	
1 space south	$1\frac{1}{2}$
1 space south-west	$1\frac{1}{2}$
2 spaces north-west	1
2 spaces east	$\frac{1}{2}$
1 space north	3
	$\frac{1}{2}$

5.

direction	number of right-angles
2 spaces east	
1 space south-west	$\frac{1}{2}$
1 space south	$2\frac{1}{2}$
1 space south-west	$1\frac{1}{2}$
1 space north-west	1
1 space north-east	1
1 space north	$2\frac{1}{2}$
	1

6. Answers will vary.

Areas of shapes in questions 1, 3, 4 and 5 are $2\frac{1}{2}$ squares; 5 squares; 4 squares; 4 squares

B3.6

PCM 45

1. [4, 5, 2] (or [5, 2, 4] or [2, 4, 5])
2. [4, 5, 3] (or [5, 3, 4] or [3, 4, 5])
3. [4, 5, 1] (or [5, 1, 4] or [1, 4, 5])

4. Rules [2, 3, 4] and [4, 2, 3] give the same tracks.
Rules [1, 2, 4] and [1, 3, 5] give tracks that look similar,
but are slightly different.

(2, 3, 4)

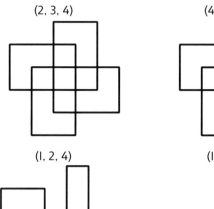

(4, 2, 3)

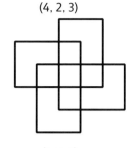

(I, 2, 4)

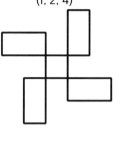

(I, 3, 5)

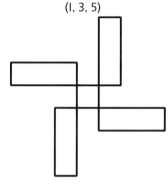

(2, 4, 4)

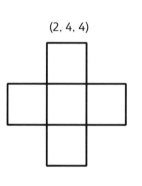

(2, 2, 7)

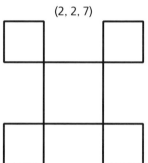

Extra

Answers will vary.
Three number sequences generate figures with rotational symmetry.
Four number sequences generate repeating figures which do not close, for example rule [1, 2, 3, 4].

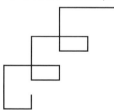

Five number sequences generate figures with rotational symmetry, for example rule [1, 2, 3, 4, 5].

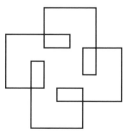

C3.I

PCM 47

Unlabelled cities on PCM map are Glasgow, Leeds, Manchester, Birmingham, Bristol

Rank	City	Country	Code	Population
1	LONDON	England	F2	7 172 091
2	Birmingham	England	E3	970 892
3	Leeds	England	E5	715 404
4	Glasgow	Scotland	C7	577 869
5	Sheffield	England	E4	513 234
6	Bradford	England	E5	467 665
7	EDINBURGH	Scotland	D7	448 624
8	Liverpool	England	D4	439 477
9	Manchester	England	D4	392 819
10	Bristol	England	D2	380 615
11	CARDIFF	Wales	D2	305 353
12	Coventry	England	E3	300 848
13	Leicester	England	E4	279 921
14	BELFAST	N Ireland	B6	276 459
15	Nottingham	England	E4	266 988

E3 Birmingham and Coventry total population 1 271 740
E4 Sheffield, Nottingham and Leicester total population 1 060 143
E5 Leeds and Bradford total population 1 183 069
D4 Liverpool and Manchester total population 832 296

Extra

Answers will vary.

C3.2

PCM 48

A10 B10 C10 D10 E10 F10 G11 H12 I11 J11 K11
L12 M12 N11 O11 P11 Q11 R11 R10 R9 S8 S7
S6 S5 S4 S3 T3 S3 R3 Q3 P2 O3 N3
M3 M4 L5 K5 J5 I4 I3 I2 I1 H1 H2
G3 F2 E1 D2 E3 E4 D5 D6 C7 B8 A9

PCM 49

St John's Village (10,10)
St Helier (13, 3)
St Brelade (6,3)
St Peter's Village (7,6)

C3.3

Range	Animal
1–9 mg	ants
10–99 mg	butterfly
100–999 mg	cockroach
1–9 g	snail
10–99 g	mouse
100–999 g	pigeon
1–9 kg	rabbit
10–99 kg	human
100–999 kg	bear
1–10 tonnes	elephant

1. Answers will vary, for example a butterfly
2. Answers will vary, for example a cockroach
3. Children should put themselves in the 10–99 kg cell

C3.4

PCM 50

1. 24
2. 14
3. 100
4. 10
5. 4
6. Answers will vary.
7.

Set A

12 months	**1 year**
Half of a fortnight	**1 week**
12 of these in a year	**1 month**
60 minutes	**1 hour**
2 weeks	**1 fortnight**
7 of these in a week	**1 day**

Set B

7 days	**1 week**
60 minutes	**1 hour**
A century has 100 of these	**1 year**
60 seconds	**1 minute**
The longest has 31 days	**1 month**
24 hours	**1 day**

Set C

A little over 4 weeks	**1 month**
February often has 4 of these	**1 week**
14 days	**1 fortnight**
About 52 weeks	**1 year**
24 of these in a day	**1 hour**
A fortnight has 14 of these	**1 day**

Set D

60 minutes	**1 hour**
3 of these make a season	**1 month**
60 seconds	**1 minute**
About 52 of these in each year	**1 week**
About 365 days	**1 year**
April has 30 of these	**1 day**

C3.5

1. A year is 52 weeks and 1 day long so the weekday on January 1st/December 31st occurs once more than all the others. (2009 Thursday, 2010 Friday, 2011 Saturday). In a leap year there are two days (Jan 1st/Dec 30th and Jan 2nd/Dec 31st) that occur more than any other. (2012 Sunday and Monday)
2. January and October both have 31 days and start on the same day (except in a leap year)
3. Answers will vary according to the year.. 2009 February, March, November; 2010 August, 2011 January, October; 2012 January, April, July.
4. Monday
5. The numbers increase by 7 each time.
6. They would still increase by seven.
   [top right] × [bottom left] − [top left] × [bottom right] = 7

Extra

Leap years occur every four years.
A leap year is divisible by 4 but not by 100. If a year is divisible by 4 and by 100, it is not a leap year unless it is also divisible by 400.
Year 2000 divisible by 400 so a leap year
Year 2100 divsible by 4 and 100 but not 400 so NOT a leap year
Year 2200 divsible by 4 and 100 but not 400 so NOT a leap year
Year 2300 divsible by 4 and 100 but not 400 so NOT a leap year
Year 2400 divisible by 400 so leap year

C3.6

PCM 5I

Answers will vary.

D3

D3.I

1. 52 + 29 + 18 + 84 + 73 + 36 = 292
2. 51 + 17 + 28 + 83 + 94 + 46 = 319
3. 27
4. 611
5. Answers will vary.
6. Maximum score 798

6	8 or 7	3 or 2
8 or 7	9	5 or 4
3 or 2	5 or 4	1

Extra

Answers will vary.
The largest score comes from numbers placed in this order (where $a > b > c > d > e > f > g > h > 0$)

d	b or c	g or h
b or c	a	e or f
g or h	e or f	0

D3.2

PCM 52

1.

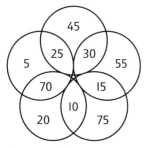

2. Answers will vary.
3. 200
4. 150
5. Answers will vary.
6. Answers will vary.
7. Largest score 470

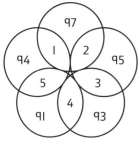

8. Answers will vary.

Extra

Answers will vary.

D3.3

1. H4; E2; S6; T8; B1;   426 + 842 = 1268
2. I9; D1; T2; O0   9 + 191 = 200
3. N7; O4; T9; L1   74 + 74 + 944 = 1092
4. S9; E5; N6; D7; M1; O0; R8; Y2 9567 + 1085 = 10 652
5. Answers will vary.
6.

```
    F  O  R  T  Y        2  9  7  8  6
       T  E  N              8  5  0
 +     T  E  N        +     8  5  0
    ─────────────       ─────────────
    S  I  X  T  Y        3  1  4  8  6
```

7.

```
    T  H  R  E  E        8  4  6  1  1
    T  H  R  E  E        8  4  6  1  1
       T  W  O              8  0  3
       T  W  O              8  0  3
 +        O  N  E     +        3  9  1
    ─────────────       ─────────────────
 E  L  E  V  E  N     1  7  1  2  1  9
```

Extra

Answers will vary.

D3.4

PCM 53

1. 225 and 425
2. 150 and 650
3. 225 and 475
4. 315 and 745

5. Set A

Number	Difference	Answer
500	175	325
325	170	155
155	560	715
715	385	330
330	315	645
645	145	500

6. Set B

Number	Difference	Answer
500	350	150
150	80	230
230	555	785
786	140	645
645	230	415
415	85	500

Set C

Number	Difference	Answer
500	85	415
415	265	159
150	795	945
945	320	625
625	95	530
530	30	500

Set D

Number	Difference	Answer
500	270	230
230	645	875
875	230	645
645	495	150
150	225	375
375	125	500

Extra

Answers will vary.

D3.5

1. 118
2. 126
3. 51
4. 281
5. 478
6. 137
7. 70
8. 44
9. 32
10. 221
11. 79
12. 235
13. Children should show that the difference between two numbers is not changed by moving both numbers an equal amount along the number line.

Extra

Answers will vary.

D3.6

PCM 54

How much does each DVD cost?
£15.99 − £2.50 = £13.49
£13.39 − £2.50 = £10.89
£12.99 − £2.50 = £10.49
£12.49 − £2.50 = £9.99

How much money is left?
£8.50 − £3.99 = £4.51
£8.50 − £4.49 = £4.01
£8.50 − £5.39 = £3.11
£8.50 − £6.99 = £1.51

How much money is saved?
£25.99 − £19.50 = £6.49
£15.49 − £12.50 = £2.99
£65.75 − £48.95 = £16.80
£35.50 − £19.98 = £15.52

Differences
Answers will vary.

E3

E3.I

PCM 55

1–4

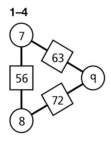 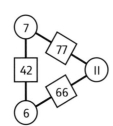

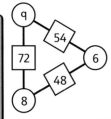 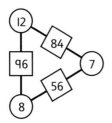

5. Answers will vary. For example

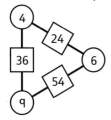

6. There is only one possible solution.

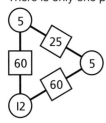

7. There is only one possible solution.

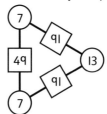

9. Answers will vary.
10. Answers will vary.
11. Answers will vary.
12. Answers will vary.
13. Answers will vary.

Extra

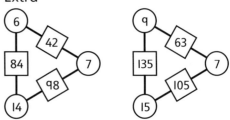

E3.2

Children create their own multiplication tables.

×	5	10	15
2	10	20	30
3	15	30	45
4	20	40	60

E3.3

PCM 56

1. 80
2. 180
3. 600
4. 800
5. 3000
6. 6000
7. 5
8. 36
9. (a) **28** 30 ÷ 10 → (d) **3** 60 × 40 → (e) **2400** 5 × 100 →
   (b) **500** 80 ÷ 4 → (missing) **20** 270 ÷ 9 →
   (c) **30** 280 ÷ 10 → **28**

Set A
70 800 ÷ 1 → **80** 40 × 3 → **120** 600 ÷ 30 → **20**
25 ÷ 10 → **2·5** 40 × 50 → **2000** 350 ÷ 5 → **70**

Set B
70 180 ÷ 6 → **30** 9 × 1000 → **9000** 500 ÷ 100 → **5**
3 × 500 → **1500** 60 ÷ 100 → **0·6** 7000 ÷ 100 → **70**

Set C
70 8000 ÷ 1000 → **8** 4800 ÷ 80 → **60** 0·4 × 10 → **4**
2000 × 4 → **8000** 40 × 10 → **400** 560 ÷ 8 → **70**

Set D
70 500 × 10 → **5000** 3·6 × 100 → **360** 100 × 3 → **300**
600 ÷ 20 → **30** 90 × 3 → **270** 0·7 × 100 → **70**

Extra

Answers will vary.

E3.4

1. Right-angled triangles
2. Cut each right-angled triangle into two more right-angled triangles
3. Answers will vary.
4. Answers will vary.
5. Answers will vary
6. Answers will vary.

Extra

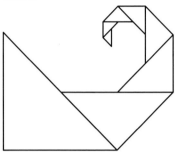

E3.5

PCM 57

1. $\frac{1}{2} = \frac{2}{4} = \frac{3}{6}$
2. $\frac{2}{3}, \frac{3}{4}, \frac{4}{6}, \frac{3}{5}$
3. $\frac{2}{6}, \frac{1}{4}, \frac{2}{5}, \frac{1}{3}$
4. $\frac{1}{4} = \frac{2}{8} = \frac{3}{12} = \frac{4}{16} = \frac{5}{20} = \frac{6}{24}$ etc
5. Answers will vary.
6.
   $\frac{2}{4} = \frac{3}{6}$ $\frac{3}{5} = \frac{6}{10}$ $\frac{1}{5} = \frac{4}{20}$

   $\frac{5}{6} = \frac{20}{24}$ $\frac{2}{3} = \frac{6}{9}$ $\frac{3}{8} = \frac{9}{24}$

   $\frac{3}{4} = \frac{6}{8}$ $\frac{7}{8} = \frac{21}{24}$
7. Answers will vary.
8.
   £3·17 + 86p = £4·03   £3·02 + 97p = £3·99
   £3·09 + 77p = £3·86   £2·96 + 89p = £3·85
   £2·85 + 97p = £3·82   £3·02 + 76p = £3·78
   £2·73 + 94p = £3·67   £2·81 + 83p = £3·64
   £2·88 + 67p = £3·55   £2·74 + 72p = £3·46

Extra

Set B

£3·17 − 89p = £2·28   £3·02 − 77p = £2·25
£3·20 − 97p = £2·23   £3·09 − 94 = £2·15
£2·96 − 86p = £2·10   £2·88 − 79p = £2·09
£2·84 − 67p = £2·17   £2·81 − 76p = £2·05
£2·85 − 83p = £2·02   £2·73 − 72p = £2·01

Set C

£3·09 + 86p = £3·95   £3·20 + 72p = £3·92
£2·88 + 97p = £3·85   £2·85 + 94p = £3·79
£2·74 + 83p = £3·57   £2·73 + 79p = £3·52
£3·17 − 77p = £2·40   £3·02 − 76p = £2·26
£2·81 − 67p = £2·14   £2·96 − 89p = £2·07

E3.6

1. 138 pennies
2. 316 pennies
3. $84\frac{1}{4}$ pennies
4. 72 pennies
5. 24 pennies
6. 23 pennies

Extra

2.4 old penny = 1p
Sixpence = $2\frac{1}{2}$p
1 shilling = 5p
1 florin = 10p
1 crown = 25p